Harry Phillips – 1796

INTER-
NATIONAL

ART SALES

1961

Edited by George Savage

STUDIO BOOKS : LONDON

Published in London by Studio Books (Longacre Press Ltd), 161 Fleet Street, EC4
Made and printed in Great Britain by William Clowes & Sons Ltd London and Beccles

contents

REVIEW OF THE ART MARKET — 7

NOTABLE SALES AND PRICES REALISED — 17

PRICE TRENDS IN THE PRINCIPAL CATEGORIES — 61

ILLUSTRATED CATALOGUE OF IMPORTANT SALE-ROOM ITEMS — 67

TRADE DIRECTORY — 145

INDEX AND LIST OF ILLUSTRATIONS — 147

review of the art market

*I*n the course of an article in the *Studio* at the beginning of the year I forecast a considerable rise in prices for antiques and works of art during the Season. Whilst this forecast did not require an unusual degree of prescience, it was certainly confirmed by subsequent events. A useful yardstick to the extent of this appreciation was the appearance in the sale-room of a number of things which had been sold a few years earlier. In almost every case large gains were noted—sometimes amounting to a doubling or trebling of former prices.

The experience of both dealers and sale-rooms has been that a greater number of people are buying works of art than ever before, and that they are by no means confined to the wealthier classes. There was, however, no significant change in the kind of things most in demand; but, in passing, the increased interest in rare books of all kinds is worth recording, although this volume is hardly concerned with them.

It is difficult to think of a time when the art market was more buoyant or more stable. The Budget, and the subsequent credit 'squeeze', which caused some equities to be marked down heavily and gilt-edged stocks to reflect investors' opinion of the financial probity of the Government, seemed, if anything, to give it a distinct fillip. This was particularly reflected in the remarkable prices realised at the Blohm Sale at Sotheby on 4th and 5th July, discussed elsewhere in more detail. A set of fifteen Italian Comedy figures of Fürstenberg porcelain, modelled by Simon Feilner, made £15,000, and other prices were in ratio.

Equally good were the prices realised for some Impressionist and post-Impressionist paintings. The number coming on to the market were, in fact, considerably fewer than the number of prospective buyers, who tended to turn their attention to works by contemporary and near-contemporary artists in consequence. With a few exceptions, however, these prices were no more than a reflection of the interest now being shown in 19th-century French painting of this kind, and a continuation of a process which has been going on since the 1880s.

The death of Sir Jacob Epstein brought some of his work into the sale-room. Those who were sufficiently far-sighted to buy whilst he was still a controversial figure must have been exceedingly gratified by the extent of the increase in value—in some cases almost tenfold for well-known portrait busts in bronze.

Nevertheless, cautious buyers must question whether the market is as strong as prices realised make it appear. To form a judgement likely to be confirmed by events, it is necessary to look not only at present-day tendencies in other fields but to the past.

Since 1914 inflation of almost all the major currencies has been a feature of public and international finance. This has been particularly noticeable since the calculated German inflation of 1924, when governments realised that they had to hand a comparatively easy way of reducing internal indebtedness without outright repudiation. Of course, an attempt is made to keep the process under some sort of control, such as the manipulation of Bank Rates, and periodic credit 'squeezes', but the printing-press is so easy a method of financing ever-increasing government expenditure that it is doubtful, today, whether any government wishes to arrest the process entirely. During the year one or two commentators aptly described government stock as 'guilt-edged', and the election of a Democratic President in the U.S.A. made a further bout of inflation in that country a distinct possibility.

It is not surprising, therefore, that investors are increasingly turning their attention to things which can not only produce an excellent return on their money but which have the virtue of being comparatively free from bureaucratic control, as well as from nationalisation and various forms of political expropriation. In addition, in the United Kingdom at least, profits from the sale of antiquities and works of art by collectors are capital gains, and therefore not subject to income tax.

To this extent, therefore, world events have created a favourable climate for a stable and rising market, which seems likely to endure whilst private investment of any kind forms part of the structure of international society.

If due allowance is made for the decrease in the value of money, it is very doubtful whether prices are yet historically high. Price-levels before the war of 1914–18 were generally a good deal higher, if the figures are adjusted to compensate for the alteration in the value of currency. In many cases, when this is done, prices are seen to have been much higher then, although not always for the same things.

Despite this, it became the custom in a number of quarters before the end of the year to refer to 'sensational' prices, and to a 'boom' in works of art. This was due, no doubt, to a predilection for superlatives on the part of the popular press, but it also argues a lack of knowledge of the past. The spate of books on the aesthetic appreciation of the arts continued unabated, but there was almost nothing on the equally fascinating and important subject of the economics of acquiring such objects.

The truth is that it is not the prices which are exaggerated but currencies which have been devalued. The man who earned £5 a week before 1939 can just about preserve the same standard of living on £17 10s., whilst the work of art which sold for £500 before the last war is not excessively priced today at £1,750. In terms of currency values before 1914–18, these figures would rise to at least £25 and £2,500 respectively. That these figures are not exaggerated was proved when the question of rents became one of the year's most bitter controversies. It was freely admitted that pre-1939 rents needed to be multiplied by $3\frac{1}{2}$ to express them in terms of today's currency, and the use of a factor of 5 to calculate values prevailing before 1914–18 does not need defending.

Nevertheless, the legend of 'sensational' prices dies hard. Not the least amusing by-product towards the end of the year attributed them to large and sinister purchases by the Soviet Premier, and a columnist in a national newspaper recorded the opinion that this was part of a dark economic plot to ruin the capitalist world.

It would not, of course, be surprising to learn that Mr Krushchev was buying works of art, and the Soviet Government is, presumably, at least as interested in adding to its Museums and Galleries as those of the West. But to suggest that prices have been exaggerated in consequence to a greater degree than would have occurred if anyone else had bought the objects is irresponsible.

I can recall a mere handful of instances on which prices for important things seemed to me higher than I thought warranted, and on two of those occasions the purchases went to private collectors in countries totally unconnected with the U.S.S.R. It was suggested that bidding was being done by a corps of secret agents, but it seems to have escaped the writer that every successful bidder also has an underbidder. Unless each agent was given the same secret instructions, and they were bidding against each other, it is difficult to see how they could raise prices more than a fraction beyond that which the underbidder was prepared to give.

This is the kind of farcical situation which arises from lack of experience of the market. It is easy to turn back to the past and point to the fact that a porcelain figure sold today for £500 only made £250 in 1909, but unless the fact that the 1909 figure represents £1,250 in terms of purchasing power is remembered, the comparison is meaningless. Of course, those responsible for starting this rumour may have had in mind the extensive purchases of the Berlin Museums before the 1914–18 war, and the Czars were large buyers of works of art in western sale-rooms. The Russians were, in fact, buying Impressionist paintings in Paris in the 1890s—many years before English buyers realised that they might be worth collecting.

Current prices do not please everyone. The position of our museums and art galleries was emphasised in *The Times* in May by an article headed 'National Gallery's Plight in a Seller's Market', in which the disappearance of important works to the Continent and the U.S.A. was discussed.

The article underlined what most people in touch with the art-market have long since realised—that penal taxation, and a capital levy disguised as estate duty, have all but eliminated private gifts to Museums. The Treasury, unperturbed by the operation of Parkinson's Law going on around it, is, nevertheless, parsimonious to the ultimate degree when the arts need support. The equitable solution to the present *impasse* is to adopt a system similar to that operating in other countries. The foresight of the U.S. Congress, and the Board of Internal Revenue, has seen to it that American public Museums are filled to overflowing at a much lower cost than would have been necessary had the purchases been made from public funds. It is true that, in some cases, the taxpayer gains some small advantages, but there seems no reason why he should not.

To the private buyer in the States has been added the corporation. The Chase Manhattan Bank, for instance, now has its own art gallery in New York, and it seems that even Banks regard works of art as a suitable field for investment. It is certain that such a step would not have been taken merely to entertain the customers, and it cannot have escaped those responsible that the presence of such works acts as a tacit suggestion to its clients that, if they go and do likewise, it will have the Bank's approval. Towards the end of the year, too, the *New Yorker* recorded the fact that U.S. tax consultants are now in business as advisers on works of art. They are prepared to suggest suitable works to their clients which are worth holding for eventual capital gains, or for presentation to Museums.

This question of the use of works of art as an investment, which is increasingly becoming a feature of the market, is so much a focus of interest at present that it needs examination at greater length.

The more sceptical point to the vast purchases of American millionaires which started in the 1870s, where the subsequent losses were often more sensational than the profits. Buyers like Mrs Potter Palmer of Chicago, who was largely responsible for New York's first exhibition of Impressionist painting in 1886, helped to establish modern French painting in the U.S.A. This enjoyed a certain measure of success; more, at least, than the earlier exhibition in Paris. In 1892 she bought four Renoirs for $5,000 which, today, would certainly be worth about $500,000. This, as capital appreciation, is by no means to be despised. But generally, even with the aid of the young Berenson, a good deal was bought by other collectors that would not stand the test of time and now lies buried and forgotten in the basements of American Museums. Even the great John Pierpoint Morgan, who was certainly not as gullible in matters of price as some would suggest, often paid sums which were quite unjustified, and that did not stand the test of subsequent resale.

Scholarship and expertise were at a low ebb, and attributions were more often optimistic than accurate. The Yerkes sale in 1910, for instance, was noted for the number of fakes even by the standards of the time, and a millionaire in the Middle West is reputed to have bought ten Rembrandt forgeries before he succeeded in acquiring his first genuine example, which became suspect because of its company. Then, too, there is the old gibe that Corot painted 3,000 pictures of which 10,000 are in America. The trade in fake Corots was not, of course, confined to the U.S.A. The exhibition of Dr Jusseaume's collection in 1928 revealed that of 2,414 pictures in his possession not one was genuine.

At this time dealers were opportunists rather than experts. The golden vision dangled before their eyes by men of astronomical fortune proved too much for human nature, and restrictive legislation by various governments on the export of works of art, which both customers and dealers joined in evading, lent a dubious air to the whole pastime of art-collecting.

Nevertheless, the situation was not as bad as some writers on the subject seeking to interest the general reader make it appear. Most prices were realistic enough, particularly in the realm of decorative art. The important point to those seeking to draw lessons from the past is to find a way of separating prices which were justified by the object from those which were not. For every cheque-book collector, who bought status-symbols on impulse at exaggerated prices, there were others like Lady Charlotte Schreiber in England and Charles Freer in America who studied their subject and made use of the best expert advice available. They made a few mistakes, but, for the most part, the appreciation in terms of money has, in the intervening years, more than kept pace with the devaluation of currency. It has, in fact, added a very substantial amount in the form of capital gains.

It was, however, a speculative market, with glittering prizes for those who guessed right, and equally substantial losses for the others. The following half-century has seen a gradual reconstruction of the art-market on different lines. This has had the effect of adding the element of stability which was formerly lacking. Perhaps the most important factor has been the rise of the sale-room to its present position of importance. The largest now devote much time and scholarship to attributions, although some will always be controversial. Then, too, dealers have become increasingly expert. The opportunist dealing in things hardly understood, and using them as financial counters in a game of wits with his clients, has almost disappeared. The dealer, today, plays a vital part by his purchases for stock, absorbing temporary price-fluctuations and maintaining the market.

Prices for extremely rare and important things must be unpredictable. The number of people able to pay a quarter of a million pounds for an important painting, for instance, will always be limited. A work of this kind may appear on the market at a time when there are several people willing to buy it, in which case it will make its price. It may, on the other hand, appear at an unfavourable time, when no one is interested or able to pay for it.

The market for the less important paintings, and the various kinds of decorative art, however, suffers from no such disadvantage, and these can always be absorbed without difficulty. The popularity of the sale-room as the primary method of dispersal has reduced the opportunities for a spectacular bargain almost to the point of non-existence, but the expansion of the market has also largely removed the element of risk which formerly existed.

The essential difference between the sale-room, the dealer, and the collector is in the kind of profit they seek. The sale-room charges a modest commission, and provides a central point to which works can be sent for sale. The integrity of the catalogues, despite the inevitable occasional mistake, is undoubted. The dealer's profit, too, in these days is modest because his market is much more certain. Now he looks for a profit on a steady annual turnover, rather than for a windfall on a lucky purchase. The customer, if he is wise, looks for long-term profit and capital appreciation. A good collection, got together with taste and discrimination, and held for a period of years, is almost certain to rise in value. Not only is this due to currency devaluation, but to other factors equally important. Market prices are primarily ruled by supply and demand. In the modern world, where most things which were formerly made by hand as works of decorative art are now made in factories on a production line, demand is certain to increase, whilst supply inevitably lessens. Accident, deterioration, and gifts to Museums, which will never come back on to the market, affect the supply position to the benefit of the collector.

London remains the centre of the art market, and many of the world's important collections are sent to it for dispersal. In July, 1960, at the end of the Season, Sotheby announced a final total for the year of £6,876,460 ($19,254,100), whilst, in the same period, Christie's had a turnover of £3,700,000 ($10,360,000). In New York, where, for geographical reasons, dispersals are more or less confined to American collections, the Parke-Bernet Galleries reported a total of $9,240,982 for this period.

With so great a turnover, the London auction-houses can afford to charge a lower rate of commission than their foreign counterparts, but quite important is the fact that sales-taxes are common abroad, whereas no such tax is levied in England. This, of course, is enlightened self-interest on the part of the Treasury. The value of this position in the art-market, in terms of international trade and goodwill, is far greater than whatever the imposition of a purchase-tax might bring. It is, perhaps, worth remarking that this flourishing business is also one of the least harried by bureaucratic control and taxation.

It is, therefore, reasonably safe to predict that the stability of the art-market is at least as assured as that in good equity shares, and it is far less likely to be affected by political events. In my opinion, nothing short of an international economic catastrophe, similar to that of the early 1930s, is likely to make more than a temporary difference to the present situation.

So far, these remarks have been principally concerned with important works of international interest. Most of us cannot afford paintings by Cézanne, or Louis Quinze silver dinner-services. It is, of course, quite obvious that increased prices for the finest things must, to some extent, affect objects of medium quality which exist in greater numbers. Increases, however, are not so great in proportion in this field, although appreciation is, for the most part, continuous and steady.

The collector, however, must be prepared to exercise discrimination in buying, and it is here that the ability to estimate quality becomes of great importance. In many ways the less wealthy buyer, although he cannot hope to acquire the things which are the subject of international competition, is ultimately in a more rewarding position. The fact that he cannot write cheques for large sums, and must count the cost of what he buys, lends zest to the search. Much of the interest is lost when the only obstacle to possession is a signature to a cheque on a large and uncommitted bank account.

The things hitherto discussed have been analogous to the 'blue chips' of the share market. There remains, however, one section of the art-market which is capable of paying extremely high dividends to the speculator in exchange for a comparatively small outlay—the work of living artists. This needs either good luck or good judgement, and it is, in any case, sure to be highly speculative.

There is a certain amount of substance in the charge that the work of an artist is not truly valued until he is dead, although the history of the art-market can point to many who have made substantial fortunes during their life-time. In most such cases values have dropped catastrophically afterwards, although in a few instances they have subsequently recovered. In still fewer, they suffered no serious change. As an investment which is not intended to be speculative, the purchase of the work of fashionable living artists needs careful consideration.

The principal reason for the appreciation of some artists after their death is a simple one—it is the law of supply and demand in operation. Until he dies an artist is able to supply his market. After this the sum total of his work is known, and an increasing demand can only be filled from what already exists.

The modern cult of personality, reinforced by questionable methods of publicity, needs to be regarded with the greatest suspicion and scepticism. Film-stars, singers of popular songs, and politicians are made in this way, and disappear into limbo when the glare of publicity is switched to others equally undeserving. The quality which makes a work of art valuable is the object itself, not the personality of its creator as seen by a press-agent. Then, too, unorthodox methods of applying paint to canvas may buy a little time on television circuits, but they do not, in themselves, create a work of art. The ephemeral has to be separated from things of permanent value, and only sound judgement, best obtained from a study of the past, is likely to do this effectively.

The end of the year is a popular time for prognostications, some of which have even been known to be fulfilled. Newspapers began to give advice to the Chancellor on his Budget, and, of the suggestions canvassed which would affect the art-market, a universal sales-tax and a capital gains tax need discussion, since, even if they are not imposed this year, they are a possibility to be reckoned with in the future.

The first would put the London sale-rooms at a similar disadvantage to their counterparts abroad, and it might have the effect of making foreign sellers less anxious to send their collections to London for dispersal. This would, to some extent, weaken its position in the international market. It is, however, difficult to see how a sales-tax could be levied in equity. Sales are attended by private persons and by dealers. Unless some complicated administrative arrangement were made to eliminate it, purchases by dealers would bear the tax twice—once when they bought from the sale-room, and again when they sold the object to their customer. Bearing in mind the ridiculous anomalies of purchase-tax, such a situation is by no means impossible. Nevertheless, in a situation where export markets are essential to the nation's economy, it is difficult to think that such a tax would be imposed.

A tax on capital gains would be extremely difficult and costly to collect, as the Inland Revenue know quite well. It would also lead to a great deal of ill-will, because its incidence would certainly not be limited to those against whom it was directed. The demand for it seems to proceed from a section of the community who are quite willing to make such gains from football pools, but dislike the idea of it being possible to make them in the share or property markets. For the most part they forget, conveniently, that a tax on such gains must make allowance for capital losses. It could, however, lead to the strengthening of the art-market, as well as the market in all kinds of portable property of value, since it is here that such a tax could the most easily be avoided. It would, on the other hand, bear particularly heavily on the share and real property markets, and on football pools, where the extent of the gains could be ascertained.

Fortunately, the London market is international, and trade recessions in other fields are unlikely to affect it. Exhortations to other sections of the community to plunge into an ocean of paper-work in order to export may multiply; the art-dealer regards exporting as part of his normal business, and very often a large part. The warehouses of the shipping agents will, no doubt, remain as full as ever, and foreign buyers will continue to come in large numbers. Here, at least, is a bright spot in the sorry tale of British exports for which the London sale-rooms and the English dealers deserve full credit.

notable sales and prices realised

The section which follows records prices from some of the year's more important sales. It has been impossible to include every sale, and objects have been selected for mention principally for the information they give about the movement of prices throughout the year. The information is intended to be an approximate guide to the value of the more important things, and sales have been taken in chronological order. The Index is fully classified, and should be consulted for specific purposes.

The more important sale-rooms, of course, sell a large number of objects each year at much lower prices which, in the space available, it has not been possible to mention. All of them are prepared to send catalogues of sales on subscription terms, details of which can be obtained on application to the addresses listed on page 146.

A sale of English porcelain held by Sotheby on 26th January was notable for a great deal of important Worcester. A sucrier and cover pencilled in black with a Chinese scene sold for £62; a rare junket dish moulded with scallop shell ornament, for £520; a pair of early sauce-boats, c. 1753, with double shell spouts and double handles, painted in colours, £115; a rare yellow-scale teacup and saucer decorated with exotic birds, £185; a pair of dessert dishes from the Lord Rodney service, with exotic birds in the style of Evans and Aloncle, £250; a fine dessert dish painted with horses in a landscape by O'Neale, £210; an apple-green milk-jug and cover painted by the 'sliced fruit' painter, £290; an apple-green sauce-tureen, cover, and stand by the same hand, £540; and the well-known coloured 'scratch cross' mug belonging to Dr Rhodes and dated 1754, for £720.

A pair of vases of Chinese bronze beaker form, blue-scale ground and exotic birds, made £130; a plate with claret cornucopiae, gilt borders, and fruit and vegetable painting (the so-called Hope Edwardes pattern), £210; a pair of plates of the 'Blind Earl' pattern, 7½″ diameter, £190; a rare 'Fable' plate by O'Neale decorated with sheep, a fox, and a dog, £190; a very rare *bleu céleste* teapot painted with fruit and flowers, £620; and a fluted dish from the Duke of Gloucester service, 9¾″ diameter, £420.

From other factories, a small Chelsea-Derby group of Abelard and Héloise, and another group of Nuns of the same period, made £300 together. A Chelsea cane-handle of the late red anchor period, representing the actress, Peg Woffington, with a serpent-tail, £140; three pairs of Chelsea plates, brown anchor mark, with Hans Sloane flowers, offered separately, £220, £200, and £260; and a coloured 'Goat and Bee' jug, triangle mark, £350. An early Bow figure of the Muse, Erato, brought £190; a Longton Hall figure of an old man emblematic of Winter, copied from the well-known Chelsea set, £140, and a rare Derby dish moulded with grapes and vine-leaves and painted with a bouquet, £110.

A collection of English and Continental miniatures of fine quality was sold by Christie's on 9th February. This was the collection of Mr H. C. Samuelson. A portrait of La Comtesse du Barry after Nattier realised £115, and Hortense, Queen of Holland, and her infant son (afterwards Napoleon III), by Isabey, signed and dated 1810, £294. £115 was paid for an enamel portrait of Princess Sobieski by C. Zincke; £105 for one of the few enamels by John Smart known to exist, Lord Macartney; £115 for Louis Seize by Jean Petitot; and £178 for another portrait of Louis by Luc Sicardi.

Of English miniatures, a portrait of Commodore Johnstone by J. Bogle realised £178; George Bolsom of the Marines by Andrew Plimer, £120; and Miss Sarah Martin by the same artist, £210. A Richard Cosway, Lord Henry Fitzgerald, realised £157, and Miss Lucy Engleheart by J. C. D. Engleheart, £147.

John, first Earl of Mexborough, by John Smart was bought for £115; Mrs William Beckford for £152; Mrs Samuel Townsend for £231; Mrs Campbell for £304; and Mahommed Ali Khan for the same figure.

Samuel Cooper also brought excellent prices, Richard Cromwell selling for £204; Charles II for £525; Mistress Katherine Chadwick for £315; Mary Fairfax, Duchess of Buckingham, for £346; and Bridget Cromwell for £399. Queen Anne by Lawrence Cross was sold for £336; King James II by Penelope Cleyn, £273; and Elizabeth Stuart and Frederick of the Palatinate by Alex. Cooper for £273.

A portrait of James I by Isaac Oliver realised £294; Arabella Stuart by Peter Oliver, £262; and Anne, Queen of Denmark, by Nicholas Hilliard, £399.

The popularity of antique watches among collectors was tested on 16th February when Christie's sold the collection of Mr P. W. Pegge. A gold quarter-repeating watch by Bréguet realised £178; a verge watch by Pr. Dupont, London, in tortoiseshell and gold case, £126; a verge by And. Dunlop, London, with date aperture, £65; an important watch by Bréguet with a dial for the minutes and another for hours, similar to a watch sold to George IV in 1825 for 2,900 francs, £577; a carriage quarter-repeating watch by Ferd. Berthoud for £105; a verge by Thos. Tompion in metal gilt case, £57; a verge by Will. Bertram, London, with six-hour dial, in plain silver case, £126; a gold watch by Thos. Earnshaw, London, of 1807, £142; another of 1801 by Jn. R. Arnold, London, for £131; another of 1824 by Thos. Cummins, London, for £126; a chronograph by Jph. Oudin of Paris, in silver case, £178; a Swiss Jacquemart watch by Bordier of Geneva, with a man and woman striking quarters and hours, in gold case, £105; a very rare gold quarter-repeating watch signed *Etabt. Mixte de Bréguet*, for £126; a gold quarter-repeater by Bréguet, £231; and another, also in gold case, for £105.

Later in the year a calendar watch by Bréguet sold for £220. In another sale on 14th June a remarkable watch by Thos. Tompion in a gold and enamel case sold for £756; another unusual watch by Bréguet, £357; and a French watch of *c.* 1690 by F. Beronneau for £399.

Some interesting silver was sold at Christie's on 17th February, the highest price, £1,050, being for an important spoon of 1514 (Henry VII) in unusually fine condition. £500 was paid for six George I three-pronged table-forks by Andrew Archer of 1715 and nine William III rat-tailed table-spoons of 1699 by Anthony Nelme. A George II plain octagonal salver by Pezé Pilleau of 1730 (42 oz.) sold for £1,250; a Queen Anne coffee-pot by William Denny of 1702 (12 oz.), £440; a George II spherical teapot by Kenneth MacKenzie, Edinburgh, of 1733 (24 oz.) for £500; a pair of James II salvers by Thomas Bolton, Dublin, of 1685/7 (31 oz.) for £480; and a large Norwegian pear-shaped coffee-pot of rococo style from Bergen (1789) for £700.

A set of eight mahogany open armchairs with lyre-shaped splats, about 1780, and probably made by Chippendale's eldest son, also Thomas, sold for £5,775 at Christie's on 25th February. This seems to be a record price for a set of chairs of the kind. An excellent pair of Chinese mirror pictures of a youth and a girl in a landscape, period of Ch'ien Lung, sold for £1,575, and a single mirror picture of the same period in a well-carved rococo frame for £1,050. A set of five panels of English tapestries, probably Mortlake, woven with mythological subjects, realised £2,940, whilst a fine Sheraton commode (*Louis Seize à l'anglaise*) sold for £945.

At Sotheby on the same day £3,900 was paid for a silver spice-box of 1599 in the form of a scallop shell, whilst a plain two-handled cup by Paul de Lamerie of 1726 made £680. A cake-basket by Eliza Godfrey of 1784 sold for £510, and a pair of salvers by Frederick Kandler for £420.

On 27th February Sotheby sold important textiles, a Soho landscape tapestry by Paul Saunders realising £900. Two 16th-century hunting tapestries from Tournai sold for £670; two Mortlake tapestries for £530; and a silk rug of 1745 from Azerbaijan for £800. A very finely-woven Indo-Persian rug made £360. A pair of narrow Chinese tables in red lacquer sold for £360, and four Queen Anne walnut chairs for £560. A barometer by Daniel Quare realised £280.

The dispersal of a collection is always the best time at which to estimate price trends, and those interested in English pottery had such an opportunity on 1st March, when the first portion of the collection of the late F. Stacey Hooker came under the hammer at Sotheby. This consisted of 92 lots devoted to Toby jugs of all kinds.

Typical of the prices realised are £52 for a fine Astbury-Whieldon Toby; £40 for a Ralph Wood specimen; £58 for a Ralph Wood miniature, $6\frac{1}{2}''$ in height; £34 for a Ralph Wood Bacchus jug; £42 for a Whieldon 'Martha Gunn' Toby; and £60 for an Enoch Wood 'Squire' Toby.

The highest price of the day was £220 for a large 'Prince Hal' jug 16" in height. This was a fine specimen of an extremely rare model.

The inference to be drawn is that the Toby jug continues in favour among collectors, and it retains its popularity through the years surprisingly well.

A sale of more than passing interest was held at Sotheby on 8th March. This was devoted to the noted collection of Islamic pottery formed by the late Sir Eldred Hitchcock, and was the first dispersal of importance of the kind to be held for many years. It was, therefore, an excellent opportunity to judge the extent of demand. Many of the lots offered were of fine quality, and prices revealed a quickening of interest in this somewhat esoteric field.

An inscribed Samarkand bowl of the 9th century in black over a white slip ground made £420, and another slightly later, more elaborately decorated in red, black, and brown with palmettes, cypresses, and angular Kufic characters, sold for the same price A Rayy deep bowl of the 12th/13th century, which had a turquoise interior and an exterior with a band of the running neskhi script in turquoise against a black ground, was sold for £300, whilst a fine blue glazed ewer of the same period made £330. Most of the items sold for less than £100, although they were, for the most part, well above what might have been expected from prices realised when these wares appear in small quantities in general sales.

Eleven lots of Turkish pottery at the end of the sale were also sold at enhanced prices.

Typical Isnik dishes of good quality with floral decoration were in the region of £40, an especially fine example selling for £65. A good jug of the 16th century, painted with floral motifs, realised £190.

It is, therefore, fair to draw the conclusion that collectors are becoming more interested in this extremely colourful and important section of the ceramic art.

In a silver sale on 10th March at Sotheby, a two-handled cup and cover of 1744 by Paul de Lamerie in the rococo style realised £2,500, and another of 1745, £1,550. A small dish by the same maker, of 1752, was sold for £1,750, and an inkstand of 1733 for £1,800. A pair of salvers of 1717 by Pierre Platel went for £2,200; a caudle cup and cover of 1626 for £2,000; and a Monteith of 1699 by Thomas Parr for £1,050.

French furniture continued to be in demand throughout the year, and high prices were paid for fine specimens sent to Christie's by the Dowager Lady Foley and Lord Hillingdon which were sold on 17th March. The total for the day was the record figure of £101,960, although nothing reached the exceptional price of £35,700 realised in the same sale-room in November, 1958, for a marquetry writing-table of the Louis Quinze period by J. F. Oeben. This still remains the highest price ever given for a piece of furniture.

Included in the sale on 17th March, however, was a remarkable three-tiered *table à ouvrage*, also signed by Oeben, who was a pupil of Charles Joseph Boulle and numbered both Riesener and Leleu among his assistants. This returned to Paris in exchange for £13,650, and when it is compared for quality and importance with the first item mentioned, it is fair to assume that the previous price of £35,700 might well have been surpassed had this been offered in the same sale.

An important signed Louis Quinze *bureau plat* by P. Migeon, one of Mme de Pompadour's favourite cabinet-makers, made £8,400, and prices for the remainder were in ratio.

A sale at the Dorotheum in Vienna on 17th March of almost a thousand lots included an Adriaen Brouwer, *Bauern im Wirtshaus*, oil on panel, monogram, which realised Sch. 50,000 (£677); a Cornelis de Man, *Der Besuch des Arztes*, canvas, formerly in the Kaiser Friedrich Museum, Berlin, Sch. 45,000 (£609); *Der Sautanz*, by Adriaen van Ostade, panel, Sch. 65,000 (£880); two Jacob van Ruysdael's—*Kühe an der Waldfurt* and *Kühe am Waldweiher*—monogram JVR, the first dated 1660, Sch. 50,000 (£677) each; and an engraving by Matisse, coloured, *Odalisque*, Sch. 5,000 (£68). A group of four figures, carved in pine, from the Tyrol, end of the 15th century, of Christ, John, Jacob, and Peter, the three Apostles symbolising the three Ages of Man, sold for Sch. 100,000 (£1,354); and a baroque carved-wood group of two *putti* as torch-holders, Sch. 16,000 (£217). A Dutch *vitrine* in the baroque style, decorated with floral marquetry, sold for Sch. 25,000 (£338); a late baroque commode in walnut, decorated with marquetry, *c.* 1750, for Sch. 20,000 (£270); and a wooden figure of Osiris, damaged, Egyptian, about 1000 B.C., for Sch. 20,000 (£270). A baboon in basalt of about the same date made Sch. 4,500 (£61).

£4,200 was given for a Van Goyen of *Valkof Castle, Nijmegen* at Christie's on 18th March, and £892 for *St. John the Baptist preaching* by Breughel. A landscape by the same artist sold for £1,890; *Tobias and the Angel* by Abraham Bloemart for £1,155;

a kitchen interior by de Hoogh for £840, and a portrait of a small girl by Cuyp for £609.

Several Turners were offered at Christie's on 20th March and sold well. A large water-colour of the Lake of Lucerne realised £11,550, and a smaller of the Lake of Zug for £11,025. Another of Windermere sold for £2,625. A Lucas Cranach, *Adam and Eve*, was bought for £6,510, and a view of Rome by Charles F. de Lacroix for £2,730.

In a sale of old Master paintings and drawings of 23rd March Sotheby offered Gainsborough's portrait of Mr & Mrs Robert Andrews in the Park at Auberies, Sudbury, which, even to one inclined to view English portraiture with a jaundiced eye, was an event of singular importance. This picture, unknown to the public until it appeared in the Ipswich Bicentenary Memorial Exhibition of 1927, was followed by two closely-printed pages of international exhibitions where it has been shown since, and of books in which it has been illustrated. Not unexpectedly it fell to Agnew for £130,000 and was later bought by the National Gallery for an undisclosed price—perhaps about £140,000. Agnew skimmed the cream of the sale, and, for them, a satisfactory day's work included the acquisition of the magnificent Rembrandt portrait of a man, signed and dated 1633, at what must surely be regarded as the modest price of £40,000. This, and the portrait of a young woman done in the following year, came originally from the collection of the Earl of Beauchamp at Madresfield Court. The latter went to another buyer at £22,000.

A little surprising at the time was the price of £17,000 paid for a Stubbs portrait of a white poodle in a punt, which had been included in the 1958 Exhibition, *The Age of Rococo*, at Munich. But the price was confirmed by events later in the year. On 7th December £20,000 was paid at Sotheby for a portrait of the Baron de Robeck riding in Hyde Park, and a much earlier picture of Mr & Mrs Wilson at the hunt made £4,000.

The work of George Morland also made higher prices than might have been expected. *Smugglers*, a coast scene of 1792, was sold for £1,800, and a coast scene with fishermen of 1793 for the same price. A typical farmyard scene of 1792 went for £1,300, and the interior of a stable of 1792 for £500.

Two Canalettos, *A view of S. Giorgio Maggiore* and *A View of the Redentore*, realised £32,000 and £20,000 respectively, whilst a characteristic flower-piece by Jan van Huysum was sold for £5,500. A typical Oudry, signed and dated 1745, of a gazelle and hounds made £8,800.

A number of drawings at the beginning of the sale included a fine Rembrandt in pen and ink and brown wash, *The Angel Threatening Balaam*, at £4,800; a Lancret, a seated woman in black chalk heightened with white on buff paper, at £550; and a Fragonard, *Le Baiser à la Fumée*, originally in the collection of the Baron Vivant-Denon, at £1,700.

Excellent prices were given in a sale of silver at Sotheby on 24th March. A Queen Anne coffee-pot of 1711 by John Read made £2,200; a set of three scallop shells of 1732 by Paul de Lamerie, £3,200; an oval inkstand of 1749 by the same maker, £3,600; a large dish of 1707 by John Chartier, £4,100; a William III cup and cover of 1696, £4,800; and a small Elizabethan cup and cover, London, 1590, for £6,500. The collection, made during and immediately after the war, was said to have cost less than

£19,000 and realised a total of £70,560, although when adjustments have been made for the devaluation of the currency the gains do not appear excessive.

On 1st April Christie's sold the collection of fifty-six pictures formed by the late Dr C. J. K. van Aalst, the Dutch banker, for a total of £144,737. The prices realised testify to the continuing popularity of Dutch painting. A small Hobbema of a wooded river scene made £14,700, and a portrait of Rembrandt by his pupil, Carel Fabritius, was sold for the same amount. In a sale immediately following, eighty Dutch and Italian paintings were sold for prices which were equally good, an excellent river scene by Ruysdael making £15,750, and an important Magnasco landscape £10,500. This brought the total for the day to the extremely satisfactory figure of £308,000, even though the much-publicised Rembrandt *Juno* remained unsold at 50,000 guineas.

An interesting dispersal of Chinese porcelain and works of art belonging to Lady Grantham, the late Sir W. C. Hillier, and Sir Geoffrey King, took place at Sotheby on 5th April.

A fine 14th-century blue and white dish, $18\frac{1}{4}''$ in diameter, decorated with a sea-perch amid aquatic plants, made £1,200. A similar dish is at Istanbul, and another in the Ardebil Shrine.

The continuing popularity of Chinese figures of birds may be seen from the record price of £8,800 paid for an exceptional pair of pheasants, $13\frac{3}{4}''$ in height, made in the reign of Ch'ien Lung (1736–1795) and richly decorated in the *famille rose* palette.

A rare emerald green bowl of the reign of Chêng Tê (1506–1521) $7''$ in diameter, with a scaly five-clawed dragon painted in rich green enamel, and with similar dragons on the exterior, was sold for £380.

Bronzes in the same sale also made excellent prices. A libation cup (*chüeh*) of the Shang dynasty (1766–1122 B.C.) which originally appeared in the Eumorfopoulos sale (Sotheby, 31st May, 1940) was sold for £550, whilst a pair of mules' heads from the same collection, but of the Chou dynasty (1122–249 B.C.), made £4,800. Whilst the *chüeh* is a comparatively well-known form, the mules' heads were exceedingly rare and of remarkable quality.

Some interesting jades were included in the same sale. An Imperial boulder carving with the seated figure of a Lohan in meditation, which was inscribed on the back with a eulogy of a Lohan by the Emperor Ch'ien Lung, realised £120; a pair of boxes in the form of quails, £160; and an Imperial pale green vase with ring handles and *t'ao t'ieh* masks in low relief, £90.

The sale of modern British drawings, painting, and sculpture at Sotheby on 6th April provided an opportunity to gauge prices which does not often occur. To judge by the interest taken in this sale, which was much greater than on former occasions, demand for the work of the more important British artists is strengthening considerably. Particularly was this the case with Epstein, and the prices realised confirmed the tendency, noticeable towards the end of 1959, for prices to rise sharply. A small lead maquette of the large Christ executed for Llandaff Cathedral was sold for £800, whilst the familiar portrait busts were also in demand, that of Somerset Maugham selling for £500 and Bernard Shaw for £720. *Peggy Jean Asleep* realised £720; *Peggy Jean Smiling*, £400; *Deirdre*, £680; and *Morna*, £800. His water-colours were also in demand. *Roses*, a water-colour heightened with body colour, sold for £290, and *Holly-hocks*, a water-colour, for £210. Others ranged in price from £85 to £180.

Henry Moore was represented by two drawings for sculpture, one in pen and ink and grey wash of 1933 selling for £250, and the other in black chalk and water-colour of 1938 for £380. Four Stanley Spencers—*The Art Class* (formerly on loan to the Tate Gallery), *The Garage*, *The Design Class* (a triptych), and a *Street in Zermatt*—realised £450, £450, £500, and £1,050 respectively. A *Reclining Nude* by the same artist went for £620, and another, *Mary*, for £280.

The work of Ben Nicholson sold extremely well. *Playing Cards* realised £1,500, and *Heures de Jour*, a still-life with a bottle, plate, and mug on a table, £1,400. A Graham Sutherland gouache, *Vine Pergola*, signed and dated 1948, was sold for £460. Paul Nash was represented by several examples, of which *The Woodshed, Oxenbridge Cottage, Iden*, sold for £500.

Dieppe: a view of the Beach by Sickert went for £420, and the *Marie Bionda* for £520. An Augustus John, *The Little Kalmush* of 1920, from the Vanderbilt-Whitney Collection, realised £550, whilst a Munnings, *A Winter at Epsom*, exhibited at the Royal Academy in 1959 remained unsold.

Antiquities were sold at Sotheby on 11th April, the property of various owners. A fine Assyrian relief depicting a warrior, of the 7th century B.C., was bought for £2,700. This had once been in the collection of Layard, and went to the Birmingham Museum. An Egyptian basalt figure of Osiris of the XXVth dynasty was acquired for £980; a 7″ Etruscan bronze figure of a warrior for £440, and a Greek bronze sphinx of the 6th century B.C. for £400.

On 26th April Christie's sold some Russian icons and *objets d'art* by Carl Fabergé, the Court jeweller. A set of four rectangular icons depicting the twelve Feasts of the Russian Orthodox Church of the Stroganoff School, mid-16th century, made £504, and a Presentation in the Temple, North Russian School of the late 18th century, £89. A St George and the Dragon, painted in Moscow in the late 16th century, was sold for £168, and a somewhat later icon of Three Saints with raised silver halos, and a silver surround embossed with flowers, for the same price.

Of the works of Fabergé, a gold, rose-quartz, and enamel parasol handle realised £84, and a nephrite and enamel parasol handle with a narrow border of rose diamonds, £136. An oblong gold box, engine-turned, with relief borders and a monogram in diamonds, of the French Empire period, was sold for £399.

Austrian *objets d'art* included a silver and gilt ostrich cup, with silver legs, tail, and neck, and an agate body, 8¾″ in height, at £131, and an Austrian silver and enamel table-clock on an oblong plinth, with rock-crystal panels, and surmounted by an infant Bacchanalian finial, 7½″ in height, for £142.

Sotheby held a dispersal of Continental porcelain on 26th April, the property of various owners. The lots were mostly of medium quality, and prices are interesting for this reason.

A well-painted Meissen tankard with cover, decorated with Kakiemon flowers, sold for £92, and a Kloster-Veilsdorf *Pierrot* for £100. A *Harlequin* from the same factory made £130, and a much finer example of the same model, £280. Buyers appeared to be taking a greater interest in Thuringian porcelain, an observation confirmed by the Blohm sale later in the year. A *Miner* from Fürstenberg, after the familiar series by Feilner, sold for £85, and a Höchst miniature figure of *Columbine* for £130. A pair of Frankenthal *chinoiserie* figures from the hand of K. G. Lück realised £120, and an excellent Doccia white bust of Francis I, husband of Maria Theresa, £230. The well-known model of *Pierrot* from Meissen made £300, and a good example of the Kändler group of *Lovers*, £250. A Kändler group of *Scaramouche and Columbine* made the surprising price of £800. The model appeared later in the year and sold for £500. A *Fishwife* by Reinicke, from the set of the *Cris de Paris*, sold for £155. The boy and girl as the Sultan and Sultana from Höchst, the model by Melchior, made £185, and a goblet and cover in the baroque style of Böttger, £370. A good pair of Vincennes *cachepots*, painted with landscapes and fitted with later Worcester covers, fetched £400, whilst three Nymphenburg busts of the Seasons, the models by Bustelli, realised £260. Two small Chantilly bowls with typical Oriental decoration made £260 and £85 respectively, the former example being decorated in an unusual style. A pair of Tournai *jardinières* painted with exotic birds sold for £210, and the amusing Meissen group by Kändler, *Der Stürmische Liebhaber*, for £580. A Böttger red stoneware sugar-box, decorated with wheel-engraving and unfired colours, realised £115.

In a sale of silver on 27th April at Christie's twelve circular dinner plates with gadrooned rims, and crest and initials, by Fogelberg and Gilbert, made in 1784 and weighing, together, 204 oz., were sold for £550. A George II plain coffee-pot, the spout with shell-work and the domed cover with a baluster finial, made £180. The weight was slightly over 26 oz. A George I plain chocolate-pot, weight 24 oz., by Thomas Parr (1715) sold for £320, and a pair of William III table-candlesticks, probably by John Loughton (261 oz.), for £620. A Commonwealth two-handled porringer, with panels of chased formal flowers, the maker's mark G.S., the date 1657, and the weight 60 oz., realised £300. A plain circular salver on four hoof feet, made by John Carter in 1771, weight 39 oz., made £125. The best prices of the day were paid for a pair of three-light candelabra on circular gadrooned bases by John Schofield, with the arms of the Fitzgibbon family, and weighing 115 oz. at £1,600, and a set of four two-light candelabra with the same arms, also by John Schofield in 1781, and weighing 162 oz., which realised £2,100.

In a silver sale at Sotheby on 28th April a pair of Georgian wine-coolers (305 oz.) realised £850, and another pair (129 oz.), £350. A William III chocolate-pot (31 oz.) by Joseph Walker of Dublin sold for £680; a Charles II wine-cup (8 oz.) for £500; a large George III *épergne* by John Robins (182 oz.), £420; a Queen Anne Monteith (58 oz.) by Thomas Folkington for £400, and a Henry VIII spoon for £400.

At the end of April the Parke-Bernet Galleries in New York made sale-room history by auctioning, with the aid of closed-circuit television, a collection of fifty modern paintings and pieces of sculpture in four cities at the same time—New York, Chicago, Dallas, and Los Angeles. The works were contributed by various donors to be sold for the benefit of the Museum of Modern Art in New York, and the amount realised was $871,850 (£311,250). The highest price was $200,000 ($71,428) for the Cézanne still-life, *Les Pommes*. An important Braque of about 1914, *Composition: the Violin*, sold for $145,000 (£51,815)—a record price. The *Deux Femmes* of Picasso sold for £11,500, and the *Grand Portrait : Profil de Femme* of 1949, £13,250.

The same gallery also celebrated their sale of the superb collection of English furniture belonging to Walter B. Chrysler Jr, on 29th and 30th April, and 6th and 7th May, with an important catalogue in two volumes, copiously illustrated and annotated. Prices were good for many important items, and the sale, the most notable dispersal of English furniture for many years, attracted world-wide interest. A Chippendale mahogany tilting-top tripod table with piecrust top realised $4,500 (£1,606); a set of six George II carved walnut side-chairs, lion-paw and ball feet, $5,400 (£1,928), and a matching set of six, $5,400 (£1,928); a graceful Hepplewhite carved mahogany settee, upholstered in beige silk, $3,750 (£1,339); an Adam carved mahogany break-front china cabinet, $3,000 (£1,071); a Chippendale fret-carved and brass-inlaid mahogany aviary, $1,750 (£606); an Adam-Chippendale yew-wood and mahogany lady's *secretaire*, $3,000 (£1,071); a pair of George II carved and giltwood serpentine-fronted eaglet *consoles*, $4,500 (£1,606); a pair of Chinese Chippendale fret-carved mahogany armchairs, in Soho tapestry, $3,500 (£1,250); The Madingley Suite—a Queen Anne carved and gilded suite in *rose petit point*, with landscapes and scenes after Jan Brueghel, two settees and eight side-chairs, $17,000 (£6,070); a George II carved mahogany and black leather kneehole library-table, perhaps by William Kent, $6,000 (£2,142); a Chinese Chippendale carved mahogany break-front china-cabinet, from a design in the 'Director', $6,500 (£2,320); a richly-carved and inlaid Chippendale mahogany bow-front *bombé* commode, marble top $6,500 (£2,320); a Chippendale double-sided partner's desk in carved mahogany and black leather, $5,000 (£1,786); a Chippendale carved mahogany serpentine-fronted *secretaire*, $3,500 (£1,250); a Sheraton inlaid satinwood and mahogany break-front *secretaire*, inset with clock, $4,250 (£1,605).

During the following session a pair of Chippendale mahogany open armchairs in Soho tapestry realised $3,000 (£1,071); a George I inlaid walnut *secretaire* by John Phillips $4,500 (£1,606); a Louis Seize Armorial carpet, *c.* 1790, $3,500 (£1,250); a Queen Anne silver Monteith by John Gibbon, London, 1707, $2,700 (£964); a George II oblong silver tray by Jno. le Sage, London, 1738, $4,500 (£1,606); a pair of three-light silver wall-sconces, Hamburg, *c.* 1685, in the English style, $3,000 (£1,071); a pair of George III Waterford cut and moulded glass 3-light wall-sconces, $2,800 (£1,000); a pair of Chippendale carved mahogany open armchairs in Fulham tapestry, at one time in the House of Lords, $5,000 (£1,786); a fine pair of Chippendale commodes with serpentine fronts, similar to a design in the 'Director', $8,000 for the pair (£2,857); a pair of Chippendale fret-carved mahogany open armchairs in Aubusson tapestry $4,000 (£1,428); and another pair, similar, with some repairs, $2,800 (£1,000); a set of six superb George II carved walnut dining-chairs in brown leather, with lion-paw feet, $9,600 (£3,428), and a matching set of six from the same original source, $9,600; a Queen Anne inlaid walnut *secretaire*-cabinet with mirror doors, and another matching, $4,700 (£1,678) each; and a George II carved mahogany library table from Hamilton Palace, and its companion, $4,250 (£1,517) each.

Among the pictures, *The Grateful Father* by Nicholas Poussin sold for $5,000 (£1,786)

George Hardinge. M.P., F.R.S. by Reynolds, for $3,000 (£1,071); *Dorothea, Lady Robinson* by George Romney, 1786, for $2,500 (£893) and *Sarah Siddons* by Sir Thomas Lawrence, *c.* 1797, for $3,000 (£1,071). A pair of urns of Chinese export porcelain, bearing the Arms of the U.S. sold for $5,200 (£1,856).

A sale of Impressionist paintings at Sotheby on 4th May realised a total of £234,000, the *Grand Canal, Venice* of Monet making £19,500. A portrait of Leopold Zborowski by Modigliani went for £8,500, and the *Caryatide Verte*, a *gouache*, from the same hand, for £2,200. *Le Plage à Trouville* of Boudin, dated 1929, sold for £9,000. A head by Daumier sold for £7,000, and *Le Wagon de Troisième Classe* for £2,220. The sale was notable for the appearance in the sale-room of two anaemic water-colours by the late Adolf Hitler which sold for £280 and £320 respectively. To judge by the reaction from those present it will be some considerable time before such specimens are regarded in their correct light, as important historical material. They were certainly not works of art.

The first part of the important Greener collection of firearms was sold on 9th May by Sotheby, a fine double-barrelled percussion-cap sporting-rifle, signed *Wm. Greener*, realising £90; a rare flintlock rocket discharger with attached bayonet, a primitive *panzerfaust* of about 1800, £90; a mid-17th-century German wheel-lock sporting-rifle signed *Jacob Rot*, £100; and a pin-fire multi-chamber Harmonica shot-gun, inscribed *Invention Jarré à Paris*, first patented 1862, for £120. A rare pair of pellet-lock pistols, signed *Invention Gasset à Paris*, made £110, and a flintlock holster pistol by R. Silke, with London proof-marks, about 1660, £100. A fine pair of flintlock turn-off pistols signed James Freeman, Londini, of the early 18th century were sold for £115.

A sale of English porcelain at Sotheby on 10th May, the property of various owners, included some interesting and important things. A garniture of three small Worcester campagna vases of the Flight, Barr & Barr period, painted with panels of shells on a claret ground, realised £200, and a pair painted with landscapes, 8½″ high, £195. An interesting bowl of mid-18th-century date but uncertain provenance, amusingly inscribed with the words and music of a popular song by William Yates, made £130. A Bow 'dismal hound' was sold for £230, and a pair of an Actor and Actress, the man as Dr Baloardo from the Italian Comedy, from the same factory, for £160. A Chelsea fluted cup of the triangle period, moulded with prunus sprays, made £360, and an attractive sun-flower dish from Chelsea, £240. A Worcester deep plate of the Duke of Gloucester service, painted with fruit, made £310, whilst a plate from the same service was sold for £200. The following lot, a pair of Worcester scale-blue bough-pots painted with birds, was sold for £400.

A pair of Chelsea candlestick groups representing the Seasons, with gold anchor marks, realised £240, whilst a group of large goats from the same factory with a red raised anchor mark, probably painted at the *atelier* of William Duesbury, was sold for £290. A set of Derby *jardinières* with satyr mask handles and continuous landscapes by George Robertson realised £200, and a small *cabaret* of eight pieces, with an oval tray, painted with Derbyshire landscapes on a yellow ground by Zachariah Boreman, £310.

A Worcester teapot, cover, and stand, the teapot almost pear-shaped, with a blue-scale ground and birds painted in bright colours, sold for £310. This pattern closely resembles that of the Lady Mary Wortley Montagu service. Worcester baskets with pierced sides and twig handles sold well, a single example, 11″ wide, making £150, a set of three with a yellow ground, £490, and a pair with yellow ground, and covers and stands, £540.

Perhaps the most interesting and unusual item in the sale was a rococo Bow coffee-pot of moulded pear shape, with a dragon-headed spout and a small female mask. Not surprisingly this bore the impressed mark of Tebo, and in style it had a family resemblance to much of his work. It seems inexpensive at £250.

A sale of Renaissance jewellery at Sotheby on 17th May realised a total of £46,780 for 125 lots. It was the collection of the late Martin Desmoni of New York. A late 16th-century Italian chalcedony cameo pendant sold for £2,600; a Venetian *nef* pendant of the same date for £2,400; a Spanish reliquary pendant of about 1600, £1,050; a 16th-century German gold openwork pendant of Venus and Cupid, set with precious stones, £2,000; a mid-16th-century Italian enamelled gold hat badge, with pearls and rubies, £750; a 16th-century Augsburg pendant and two side links from a necklace, £950; and a South German pendant in the form of a mermaid, set with pearls and precious stones, of the 16th century, £3,400.

In a sale of weapons on 18th May Christie's sold an early pair of Austrian flint-lock pistols for £357; a Dutch holster pistol with an ivory stock of about 1680 for £483; an Augsburg 17th-century wheel-lock holster pistol, £152; a French flint-lock three-barrelled holster pistol, of about 1700, £336; a German early 18th-century wheel-lock sporting-rifle, £121; and a rare seven-barrelled naval flint-lock volley gun, about 1800, £142.

On the following day in the same rooms, a pair of George II gilt console tables, the supports carved as eagles with outspread wings, realised £1,522, and a set of eight Adam mahogany armchairs and two settees, £3,780. A pair of George II gilt-wood upright mirrors sold for £441, and a late 18th-century marquetry table in the style of Louis Seize, £756.

At Sotheby £800 was paid for a fine Swedish silver tankard, £480 for a pair of Swedish vases, and £135 for a Charles II three-pronged fork.

A sale of Impressionist and post-Impressionist paintings at Christie's on 20th May included the Matisse, *La Leçon de Peinture*, sold for £21,000, and a Monet, *The Water Garden, Givenchy*, for £19,950. A Corot, *Souvenir d'Italie*, a view of the Campagna, sold for £5,775; *Beach Scene at Berck*, by Boudin, £4,200; a portrait of René Blum, brother of Léon Blum, by Vuillard, of 1912, £4,410; and *The Farm at Vernon* of 1932, by Bonnard, £14,175. In the same sale the *Negro Page* of Wilson Steer sold for £1,365, and *Barnet Fair* by Sickert for £840.

A pottery and porcelain sale at Sotheby on 24th May included a fine pair of Whieldon crested birds which made the record price of £1,500, and a rare Dublin delft punch-bowl, inscribed, at £720.

On the same day a rare Italian violin by Pietro Antonio of Milan made its appearance at Christie's, and was sold for £504. Other *objets d'art* included a Swiss gold and enamel oblong box, the cover with Venus on a cloud, the sides and base in dark blue enamel, 3″ wide, which sold for £126; a Russian nephrite paste-pot in the form of an apple, with a gold and green enamel brush, by Fabergé, at £336; and another Swiss gold and enamel box with blue enamel panels, decorated with lovers in a landscape, at £231.

In the silver sale on the following day (25th May), a pair of four-light candelabra by Matthew Boulton of Birmingham, made in 1822, made £420, and a set of four circular salt-cellars, each on three mermaid feet, by David Hennel, made in 1743 and weighing 20 oz., realised £200. A Queen Anne mug of 1705, by Benjamin Pyne, weighing 9 oz., made £160. Continental silver in this sale also sold well. A pair of Louis Quinze candlesticks, 10″ high, probably by Pierre Adrien Dachery, St Quentin, made about 1770, realised £120. They weighed just over 26 oz. A Louis Quinze pear-shaped cream-jug on three feet, made about 1750 by R. A. Gambier, Paris, and weighing just over 5 oz., made £110; whilst a small Louis Treize square trencher salt, weight 5 oz., from Rouen, sold for £190. A pair of Louis Seize toilet-boxes by F. Joubert, Paris, weighing 12 oz. and made in 1786, realised £170; a Louis Seize two-handled sucrier and cover by J. C. Roquillet-Desnoyers, Paris, 15 oz., of 1776, £180; a Louis Quinze pear-shaped jug and cover, 10″ high, made about 1730, perhaps by Daniel Fréron, £560. This was provincial in origin, and weighed just over 32 oz. Another Provincial piece, a small Louis Quinze plain boat-shaped wine-taster from Calais, of about 1720, and weighing 3 oz., was sold for £290. Louis Quinze table-candlesticks made excellent prices, a pair 9″ in height, the maker JD, weighing 31 oz., selling for £400, whilst a set of four by Michel Delapierre, Paris, of 1732, which weighed 90 oz. made £1,350.

This sale was interesting for the number of important early spoons included, of which the following is a selection. James I small spoon surmounted by a female bust, c. 1614, 5¼″ long, £72. Elizabeth I spoon by J. Jones, Exeter, c. 1575, £340. A pair of Charles II seal-top spoons, Truro, c. 1660, £150. An Elizabeth I Apostle spoon surmounted by James the Less, 1559, £160. A pair of Elizabeth I spoons with lion sejant finials, 1598, £360. A Henry VIII spoon with lion sejant finial, 1532, £220. An Elizabeth I Apostle spoon surmounted by St Paul, by E. Eston, Exeter, c. 1585, £210.

A set of twelve Elizabeth I Apostle spoons, an extreme rarity, made £999. These, the Frith set of twelve from Bank Hall, Derbyshire, were sent by a New York owner.

At Sotheby a typical Russell Flint, *The Pool of Echoes*, realised £720; a *View of Eton from Windsor*, by John Varley, £1,850; *Springtime*, by Dame Laura Knight, £340; *Farm by the Sea*, by J. F. Herring, Senr, £300; and *Titania Sleeping*, an Academy exhibit of 1841, by Richard Dadd, £290.

Notable furniture belonging to the late Herbert Rothbarth was sold at Christie's on 26th May, when a George II walnut bookcase realised £3,780. A cream lacquer cabinet of the 17th century made £1,680; a Queen Anne walnut card-table, £945; four Chinese Chippendale mahogany armchairs, £1,890; a George I walnut armchair, £651, and another similar, £504. A Chippendale writing cabinet of about 1760 sold for £1,680; a pair of Chippendale mahogany *torchères*, £1,102; a Chippendale mahogany commode, £735; a set of four Queen Anne chairs, upholstered in floral Soho tapestry, £609; and an Agra carpet, 14′ 6″ × 8′ 10″, £945.

On 14th June the Galerie Charpentier sold old Masters and *objets d'art*, a Fragonard,

Le Galant surpris, a drawing in black chalk and bistre wash realising NF. 24,000 (£1,750); *Le femme au collier* by Jean-Baptiste Perronneau, in pastel, signed and dated 1748, NF. 29,000 (£2,114); a pen and wash drawing by Rembrandt, initialled *RVR*, *Jésus parmi les docteurs*, NF. 20,000 (£1,458); *Le petit musicien* of Gerard Dou, signed, on panel, NF. 13,500 (£984); a Drouais, *Le Jeune élève*, the original version of which was exhibited in the Salon of 1761 and belonged to M. de Marigny, the brother of Mme de Pompadour, NF. 37,000 (£2,698). A *Portrait de Maximilien Ier, Empereur d'Allemagne*, from the *atelier* of Albrecht Dürer, similar to the one sold later in New York for £607, made NF. 31,000 (£2,260); a well-known Fragonard, *Cache-cache*, NF. 150,000 (£10,934); the *Bords de rivière* of van Goyen, signed and dated 1640, NF. 24,000 (£1,750); the *Marine et vue du Château Loewenstein* by the same artist, on wood with some restoration, NF. 23,000 (£1,677); *La Fontaine* by Hubert Robert, NF. 20,000 (£1,458); the *Paysage d'Automne* of Salomon van Ruysdael, monogram, dated 1634, NF. 67,000 (£4,886); and *L'Alchimiste* by David Teniers the younger, signed, NF. 37,000 (£2,698). A version of the same subject as the last, by the elder Teniers, was sold in Vienna in March for £339. A Tiepolo, *Vision d'un saint personnage*, made NF. 24,000 (£1,750).

In the same sale a drawing-room suite in carved and gilded wood, period of Louis Seize, and stamped A. Jullien, brought NF. 15,500 (£1,100); four armchairs, carved and gilded, of Louis Quinze, NF. 13,000 (£948); a white and gold settee with carved *cartouches*, marked Tilliard, period of Louis Quinze, NF. 20,000 (£1,458); an elegant *commode* of the Louis Quinze period, with white marble top, NF. 21,000 (£1,531); a rare round mahogany table of the Louis Seize period, attributed to Weisweiler, NF. 35,000 (£2,552); an important *vitrine* of the same period decorated in marquetry, NF. 10,200 (£734); a marquetry *armoire* with the mark of Genty, Louis Quinze period, NF. 12,500 (£912); a pair of Louis Seize cabinets of drawers, NF. 28,000 (£2,041); an Aubusson carpet of the Directoire period, NF. 18,000 (£1,313); and an 18th-century Aubusson tapestry from a cartoon by Wouvermans, NF 11,600 (£846).

In a sale of drinking glasses, the property of Miss Williams, at Sotheby on 16th June, a very rare stippled goblet by David Wolff, of which hardly more than nine exist, sold for £220; a rare sweetmeat glass of about 1685, 6" in height, for £62; a goblet engraved with festoons and baroque motifs, of about 1700, £68; an ale-glass engraved with *Wilkes and Liberty, No. 45*, and an open birdcage, £48; a colour twist wine glass, £74, another for £50, and yet another for £56.

The most important events for many years in the realm of antique silver occurred on 16th June when Sotheby sold a Louis Quinze dinner-service of 168 pieces sent for sale by the Trustees of the will of the eighth Earl of Berkeley, of Berkeley Castle, Gloucestershire.

This remarkable service was by Jacques Roettiers, whose family came from Antwerp, and who studied under both Germain and Besnier. He married Besnier's daughter in 1734, and was appointed goldsmith to the King in 1737.

This service is the most important still surviving, and only two others are known. Many such services were sent to the Mint for coinage during the reign of Louis Quinze, or destroyed during the Revolution.

It was not, perhaps, suprising that it should make that record price of £207,000, and fell to the London dealer, Frank Partridge, after keen competition from a prominent Paris dealer. The price was the third highest ever realised in a sale-room for a single lot, the two higher prices both being achieved at Sotheby.

In Paris on 17th June the Galerie Charpentier sold modern pictures belonging to various owners. A signed pen and wash drawing by Dunoyer de Segonzac, *Versailles: la statue du Bernin*, pen and wash, signed, realised NF. 6,000 (£437); a lithograph, signed, by Albert Marquet, *Le Port de Boulogne*, a very rare artist's proof, NF. 2,300 (£168); a charcoal portrait, *Manet dessinant, vers 1869*, by Frédéric Bazille, NF. 21,000 (£1,531); *L'oiseau*, a first sketch for the lithograph by Braque, signed, NF. 28,000 (£2,041); a water-colour of Deauville, signed and dated 1929, by Dufy, NF. 18,000 (£1,313); the *Scène d'intérieur, Barcelone, 1899*, pastel and crayon varnished, signed, by Picasso, NF. 63,000 (£4,229); a self-portrait, *Frédéric Bazille à la palette, 1865*, oil on canvas, NF. 160,000 (£11,663); *Les Régates* by Jean Helleu, signed, NF. 11,000 (£802); *La Pêcheuse* by Cézanne, NF. 35,000 (£2,552); *Le Pêcheur* by the same artist, NF. 46,000 (£3,353). *La Barque*, another Cézanne, NF. 80,000 (£5,766); and still another, *Ciel entre les arbes*, NF. 39,000 (£2,843). *Les Bestiaires* of Chirico, signed, realised NF. 5,500 (£401); *Portrait de femme, 1939*, signed, by Marc Chagall, NF. 18,000 (£1,313); the *Jeunes filles avec fleurs* of 1927, signed, by the same artist, NF. 145,000 (£10,573); the *Barque échouées dans le Pont (Fauve* period), signed, by André Derain, NF. 140,000 (£10,208); the *Femme nue assise* of Dufy, NF. 20,000 (£1,458); the Gauguin, *La fiancée*, of 1888, initialled, NF. 135,000 (£9,843); the Matisse, *Paysage de Corse*, signed, NF. 62,000 (£4,146); *St. Valéry sur Somme* of Albert Lebourg, signed, NF. 12,000 (£875); *Bords de Seine* by Stanislas Lepine, signed, NF. 56,000 (£4,080); *Le Pont Royal*, by the same artist, signed, NF. 61,000 (£4,449); Joan Miró, *Composition en blanc, noir, rouge et verte, sur fond brun*, dated Summer, 1936, and signed, NF. 60,000 (£4,376); a Renoir, *Baigneuse assise s'essuyant la jambe*, signed, NF. 240,000 (£17,503); another, *La Bergère*, signed, NF. 140,000 (£10,208); another, *Portrait du Peintre H.-L., aux roses*, signed, NF. 36,800 (£2,683); the *Jeune femme appuyée sur sa main*, signed, sold with certificate, NF. 54,000 (£3,934); *La Rue de la Bonne à Montmartre*, oil on cardboard, signed, by Utrillo, NF. 35,000 (£2,552); *La Tour Pointue* by the same artist, NF. 32,500 (£2,363); the *Nu au miroir* of Felix Valloton, NF. 6,200 (£452); *Vase de fleurs* by Vlaminck, signed, NF. 43,000 (£3,135); *Marguerites dans une vase*, signed, by the same artist, NF. 59,000 (£4,299); and another, *Le champ devant la Ferme*, signed, NF. 40,100 (£2,923).

In an important dispersal of works of art on 17th June Sotheby sold the celebrated Thurible of Godric (the Pershore Censer) of the 10th century for £2,600. An important boxwood carving of Cleopatra by Baccio Bandinelli (1493–1560), who was Cellini's rival in Florence, sold for £620, and Italian bronzes also realised good prices. A Florentine group of Bellerophon and Pegasus realised £250; a bronze of Christ the Redeemer, School of Andrea Sansovino, 16th century, £250; and a large figure of Peace, 20½″ in height, by Tiziano Aspetti, £500.

A fine cut-silk Kashan rug sold for £700, and an attractive pair of Louis Seize Aubusson tapestry panels, woven with scenes from Country Pleasures, £1,000.

French furniture, as might be expected, was in demand. A fine small Louis Quinze cartel timepiece sold for £650; a Louis Seize marquetry *secretaire à abattant*, the front inlaid elaborately, 3′ 2″ wide, £780; an important pair of Louis Seize *vitrines* in Boulle marquetry by Étienne Levasseur, £6,200; a Louis Quinze *bonheur du jour* by C. Wolff, £820. £1,050 was given for a Louis Quinze tulipwood writing-table by I. F. Dubut; £3,000 for a Louis Seize kingwood commode by C. C. Saunier; £1,200 for a pair of Louis Quinze marquetry *encoignures*; £1,500 for a Louis Seize commode by Jacques van Oostenryck, called Dautriche; and £2,100 for a Louis Seize *secretaire à abattant* by P. Roussel. A very fine set of oak-panelling (*boiserie*) formerly in the Hôtel Nicolai, Paris, realised £4,000.

In the June sale at the Dorotheum a French painting of about 1420 by the Catalan Master, *Lamentation of Christ*, on panel with a gold ground, realised Sch. 75,000 (£1,016); the *Szolnoker Geschirrmarkt* of August v. Pettenkofen (1822–1899) formerly in the collection of the Graf Ludwig Károlyi, Budapest, sold for Sch. 35,000 (£475); the *Blumenstück mit Grünling*, monogram *To R*, by Tomasso Realfonso, for Sch. 32,000 (£432), and another, *Blümenstück in weissblauer Fayencevase mit Schmetterling*, monogram, for Sch. 38,000 (£516). Two pictures of the modern French school, the *Französische Kleinstadt* (*Petit ville de France*) of Vlaminck, signed, c. 1908, and the *Fischerbarken bei Saint-Malo* (*Barques de pêche à St. Malo*), water-colour, signed, of Signac, brought Sch. 250,000 (£3,385) and Sch. 38,000 (£516) respectively. A lime-wood late Gothic carving of a standing saint, polychrome, with the later addition of gold and silver, early 16th-century, brought Sch. 16,000 (£217); a baroque statue of St Elizabeth from the studio of Franz Joseph Holzingen, c. 1715, the same sum; and another of St Zacharias, a similar amount. Two fine South German standing Apostles of c. 1740, in limewood, from the Master of the Eberbach figures, sold for Sch. 32,000 (£432) and Sch. 15,000 (£203). A tankard (*Walzenkrug*) in silver, standing on three claw feet, perhaps by Johann Berend of Riga, c. 1700, realised Sch. 8000 (£108).

Christie's sale of *objets d'art* on 21st June included some important Scottish pistols. A flint-lock belt-pistol by Murdoch, in fine condition, of the late 18th century, realised £420, and the following lot, one of the most important for a considerable time in its field, was a magnificent pair of Scottish presentation pistols, probably made originally for George III, the stock set with an oval enamelled gold escutcheon of the Orders of the Bath and the Thistle. These made the not surprising price of £2,205. They were presented by the King to Sir Henry Clinton, and the price was a record for a pair of pistols.

Other objects in the sale included an Austrian rock-crystal *biberon*, enamelled with flowers and birds, 7¾″ high, at £210; a Russian triangular enamel and silver-gilt patch-box by Fabergé, at £220; a triangular soapstone and gold patch-box by Fabergé £157; and a Russian silver and nephrite inkwell ornamented with dolphins by Fabergé, £399.

An oval gold box, the cover inset with a portrait of Napoleon I and signed by Isabey, Court-Painter to the Emperor, realised £756. A tortoiseshell and gold box, with a portrait of Napoleon as a Roman victor by Lewis-Bertin Parant, 1813, was sold for £315. An English oblong gold box, c. 1720, engraved with cupids in a garden, made

£220, and a Swedish vari-coloured gold box, the cover chased with figures against a rococo pediment background, mid-18th century, £777.

Important items were included in the sale of silver on the following day (22nd June). A George I fluted circular dish by David Tanqueray of 1723, 7″ in diameter and weighing almost 12 oz., realised £250, and a George I plain pear-shaped hot-milk jug, 6″ high, from Edinburgh, and weighing about 14 oz., £320. An Elizabeth I tigerware jug, 9½″ high, with silver-gilt mounts of 1588, was sold for £280, and another, later in the sale, made £260.

Four George II table-candlesticks by James Gould, of 1738, almost 7″ high and weighing 56 oz., were sold for £500, and a two-handled boat-shaped soup-tureen and cover by Robert Makepeace, of 1794, weighing 117 oz., for £520.

The Wilbraham cup, an Elizabeth I silver-gilt cup and cover, 11½″ in height and weighing 20 oz., sold for £2,700. This, made in 1585, had the Arms of Wilbraham of Woodley, and was formerly in the possession of William Randolph Hearst. An unusual item was a Charles II toilet-mirror, chased with birds, flowers, and foliage in the Chinese style, and with figures in a landscape on the cresting. This, made about 1680 and 23″ in height, realised £540. Even more unusual was an early English spoon with a diamond point finial, 6⅜″ long, made about 1350, which sold for £1,450.

Continental silver in the same sale included a German silver-gilt pineapple cup and cover by Hanss Beutmuller, Nürnberg, made about 1600 and weighing 11 oz., at £125; a Dutch oblong salver on pierced bracket feet, 21½″ wide, by Martinus van Stapele, The Hague, made in 1785 and weighing 131 oz., at £220; a rare German silver-gilt and agate tea-service—teapot, pair of oval boxes, and four cups—from Augsburg, made about 1695, with original leather case, at £850; and a Swedish parcel-gilt cylindrical tankard and cover on ball feet, the cover with an applied plaque of the Roman Charity, by Arvid Falck, Stockholm, £1,150. This, made in 1691, weighed 52 oz.

A German silver-gilt tazza, 16¾″ high and 15″ in diameter, apparently of late 16th-century Augsburg workmanship, made £380; a Dutch tobacco-box of square form, made in Amsterdam in 1738, £250; and a Dutch octagonal brandy-bowl with engraved decoration, by Jan Melgchers Oostervelt, Leeuwarden (1635–1655), £210.

On the same day Sotheby sold old Masters for a total of £159,855. A portrait of Herman Boerhave, his wife, and children by Aert de Gelder made £15,000; a panel, *St. Benedict*, by Fra Angelico, £9,500; a Cranach portrait of Dr Johann Bugenhagen, £10,000; a *Madonna and Child* by Isenbrandt, £3,500; an *Adoration* by Pittoni, £3,200; a *Capriccio* of Canaletto, £7,500; a landscape by Jan van Goyen, 1646, £4,800; *The Bathers* of Fragonard, £4,200; and a *River Landscape*, 1633, by Salomon van Ruysdael, £3,800.

Important modern pictures were sold by the Galerie Charpentier on 23rd June. A Dufy, *Intérieur à Caldas de Montbuy (Espagne)*, a signed water-colour, made NF. 12,500 (£912); a black crayon drawing, *Tête de jeune femme*, of Modigliani, NF. 4,300 (£313); a water-colour of 1919, signed *La Table* by Picasso, NF. 23,000 (£1,677); the *Faunes et Nymphes*, a pen drawing by the same artist, NF. 10,200 (£734); the *Portrait de Renoir* of Louis Valtat, a pastel, NF. 8,000 (£582); *Eve*, a sketch in terracotta by Rodin, signed, NF. 9,100 (£663); *Les tournesols au bord de la rivière* by Caillebotte, signed, NF. 18,500 (£1,348); the *Portrait d'homme*, by Cézanne, oil on paper mounted on canvas, formerly in the Vollard collection, NF. 10,000 (£729); the *Crozant, le Pont Charrant*, of Guillaumin, signed and dated 1892, NF. 16,500 (£1,202); *La Rochelle: entrée du port*, signed, by Lebourg, NF. 12,500 (£912); the *Notre-Dame de Paris, vue du Pont de la Tournelle*, signed and dated 1911, of Loiseau, NF. 10,000 (£729); *La Femme au manchon*, in red chalk, by Renoir, initialled, NF. 65,000 (£4,375); a water-colour by Dunoyer de Segonzac, *Le Guéridon*, signed, NF. 34,000 (£2,479); the *Petite route méridionale au Cannet 1924*, signed, by Bonnard, NF. 265,000 (£18,958); *Le jardin publique*, pastel, a panel of a triptych, by the same artist, NF. 21,000 (£1,531); *Barques de pêche au mouillage*, panel, signed, by Boudin, NF. 45,000 (£3,282); the *Sortie du port de Trouville*, signed, on panel, by the same artist, NF. 31,000 (£2,260); and another, dated 1879, *Bords de mer*, NF. 31,000 (£2,260).

Les Arums, a study of lilies, by Van Dongen, signed, realised NF. 75,000 (£5,868); the *Rouen, les chalands sous la neige*, signed, by Monet, NF. 147,000 (£10,719); a Signac, *Les Andelys*, signed, NF. 102,000 (£7,437); and *L'Odet à Quimper*, signed and dated 1923, by the same artist, NF. 105,000 (£7,655). An Utrillo, *Paysage à la tour*, signed and dated 1917, made NF. 48,000 (£3,499); *Montmartre: le Moulin de la Galette et le Sacré-Cœur*, signed, by the same artist, NF. 31,000 (£2,260); *La fille aux canards* by Soutine, signed, NF. 220,000 (£16,045); a Vlaminck, *Bords de rivière*, signed, NF. 81,000 (£5,839); another, *Les femmes*, by the same artist, signed, NF. 43,000 (£3,135); *La sortie des employés* by Vuillard, NF. 30,000 (£2,188); *Le coucher* by Toulouse-Lautrec, on panel, signed, NF. 350,000 (£25,510); and *La femme au collier* of Louis Valtat, signed, NF. 18,000 (£1,313).

At a picture sale on 24th June Christie's offered a water-colour by Turner—*Orford, Suffolk*—which sold for £2,730. The bird-painter, Archibald Thorburn—was represented by several pictures done about 1910. A *Mallard Duck* was sold for £23; a *Grouse* for £42, a *Robin on a Branch*, £19; a *Partridge in Snow*, £68; a *Black-cock*, £115; and a *Grouse by a Moorland Pool*, £147.

A *Conversation Piece* by Francis Wheatley made £630; the *Death of Orpheus*, an Italianate river landscape by J. H. Mortimer, £472 10s.; the *Royal Oak* by Wm. Shayer, Senr, £651; and a pair of *Huntsmen Mounting* and *Jumping a Hedge* by David Dalby, £630.

An important sale at Sotheby on 27th June of African sculpture, some formerly in the collection of Dr R. Allman, Principal Medical Officer, Southern Nigeria, from 1891 to 1905, was remarkable for a number of fine pieces.

A Benin bronze plaque of the 17th century representing an Oba or chief in court dress was sent for sale by the Trustees of the British Museum, and sold for £900. A superb seated male figure in wood from French Equatorial Africa, 19½″ high, realised £520. An elaborately carved tusk from Benin, 70 lbs. in weight and 6′ 2″ long, with figures of warriors, chiefs, priests, birds, leopards, and the like, made £950. An impressive carved wood female figure, taken from a Ju-ju house in Southern Nigeria in 1901, realised £500, and a fine wood figure of a man seated on a stylised elephant from the Niger Delta, £640. A 17th-century ivory figure, 21″ in height, from Benin, sold for £1,800, but the finest example of primitive art to appear in the sale-room for many years, a 16th-century Benin ivory pectoral mask found in a box in King Ovonramwe's bedroom, was bought—not unexpectedly by K. J. Hewett—for £6,500.

The sale of old Masters at Sotheby on 29th June included a pair of oval panels by Boucher—*The Mill* and *The Trout Stream*—which sold for £10,500. A portrait group of the Lavie family by Zoffany realised £7,000; a white spaniel by a lake, by Stubbs, £2,800; and a landscape of 1644 by van Goyen, £3,900. Among the drawings, a Tiepolo of the Virgin and Child brought £620; one of a girl, in black chalk heightened with white, by Piazzetta, £460; and a Goya of an old woman nursing a child, £1,400.

A dispersal of French furniture occupied Christie's on 30th June and 1st July, a set of six painted *fauteuils* by J. Lebas making £7,860; a kingwood and rosewood writing table by Pierre Migeon, £2,940; a work-table, the top inset with a Sèvres plaque, £1,785; a gilt-wood *chaise longue* in cream brocade, £1,680; and a parquetry boudoir writing-table, £3,060. A pair of Louis Seize gilt-wood armchairs by J.-B. Tilliard sold for £1,417; a clock of the same period with Meissen porcelain flowers, £1,995; a pair of ormolu wall-lights, £1,365; a pair of Louis Quinze ormolu and *blanc-de-chine* porcelain candelabra, £1,312; a pair with Meissen figures by Kändler, £1,281; and another similar, £1,575. A late 18th-century needlework carpet, which may have been made in Goa for Clive when he was governor of Madras, 32′ × 20′, brought £2,995.

At Sotheby on 1st July an interesting pair of Venetian blackamoors, 4′ 5″ high, realised £370.

Christie's sale of pictures and drawings of 1st July included the work of contemporary and near-contemporary artists. A lithograph by Paul Klee, signed in pencil, *Die Hexe mit dem Kamm*, sold for £44, and an etching by Edvard Munch, *Portrait of a Man*, signed in pencil, £23. A signed drawing in charcoal and pastel, *A Man on Horseback*, by Degas, realized £121, and a portrait *Head of a Woman* in pencil and coloured chalk by Marie Laurencin, and signed and dated 1947, £89. A *Female Nude*, in pencil with monogram, by Aristide Maillol, made £58; a *Woman with Folded Arms* in pen and black ink by Matisse, £31; and *Nue Allongée*, in pencil and water-colour by Rodin, £63. *Reflections*, in pencil and initialled, by Tissot, sold for £63, and a *Study of a Nude Woman* by Renoir in black chalk, for £168. Four Sickerts were included—*Nude lying on an iron bedstead* in black chalk heightened with white on violet paper, £50; *View of Church and Street in Dieppe*, black chalk and pen and black ink on brown-toned paper, £157; *The Venetian Shawl*, similarly executed, £100; and *La Hollandaise*, a standing full-length nude, signed, in black chalk on brown-toned paper, £105.

Among the paintings, two by Sir Matthew Smith, *Tiger Lilies* and a *Portrait of a Man*, made £252 and £210 respectively. Sir Alfred Munnings was represented by *Hop Pickers Returning* and *Man Asleep by a Team of Horses* at £735 and £1,050. Two paintings by Augustus John, *Sweet Williams* and *Tower and Sky*, sold for £399 and £294.

Epstein was represented by both drawings and bronzes. *Portrait of a child with top*, in pencil, signed, sold for £68; *Study of a Recumbent Nude Negress*, in pencil, signed, £58; and a sketch of *Child with clasped hands*, in pencil, signed, £105. The bronze portrait of the Emperor Haile Selassie made £504; a *Head of an Infant*, £210; and a portrait of Sholem Asch, £819.

In the morning sale of 6th July Sotheby sold paintings belonging to the late Ernest Duveen. Unlike his brother, Ernest Duveen bought modern paintings, and this collection, assembled with taste and skill, was proof—if it were needed—that a combination of good judgement and a little luck can be extremely profitable. It was estimated at the time that this collection had cost Duveen about £20,000, and the result of the morning's work was £134,130. *Le Givre*, by Monet, sold for £8,000; *Jeune fille au chapeau verte* of Mary Cassat, £7,500; a Renoir, *Paysage de Cagnes*, for £3,200; Modigliani's *Portrait de jeune fille* for £24,000; the *Notre Dame* of Albert Marquet for £5,200; *Le jardin du peintre* of Bonnard for £9,000; a Chagall, *Grand bouquet de fleurs*, for £12,800; a Ben Nicholson, *Roof Tops, St. Ives*, of 1948, for £1,700; *Bouteille, poire et cruche*, by Nicholas de Staël, for £9,200; *Peinture, noire et verte*, by Hans Hartung, for £4,200, and a *Composition* of 1958 by Pierre Soulanges for £3,000.

The afternoon sale, the property of various owners, also showed some notable prices. The *Cheval au galop sur le pied droit*, a bronze by Degas, realised £5,100; *Romeo et Juliette*, white marble by Rodin, £5,500; *Femme Nue*, by Bonnard, £18,000; *La Barque Pavoisée* of Braque, £9,500; *Les Lavandières* of Sisley for £11,000; *Les Ivrognes*, by Cézanne, £10,000; *Mère et enfant* of Renoir, £38,000; Modigliani's *Portrait of Beatrice Hastings*, £10,000; the Picasso, *Trois Baigneuses*, £6,000; a van Gogh drawing of his garden at Arles, in pen and ink, £4,000, and a Gauguin, *La Côte Bretonne*, £9,000.

On 7th July Sotheby sold the collection of John Rewald of New York, author of a standard work on Impressionism. His collection of drawings, in 137 lots, realised just over £96,000. A pencil portrait of Mme Cézanne by Cézanne sold for £1,100; a Daumier, *Têtes de deux hommes*, in pen and ink, £1,520; the *Jeune femme assise avec éventail*, pencil and coloured chalk, by Degas, £3,800; a gouache, *Les Folie de l'Amour*, of Gauguin, £2,200; the *Tahitienne accroupie*, a monotype by the same artist, £3,000; the *Vieillard avec parapluie, vu de dos*, in pencil, of van Gogh, £3,800; another of the roofs of Arles, in pencil and reed pen, also by van Gogh, £5,000; the *Nature Morte* of Juan Gris, a water-colour, £2,000; the *Indischer Blumengarten* of Paul Klee, a gouache, £4,000; a Matisse, *Portrait de fille de l'artiste, Marguerite*, pen and ink, for £3,000; a pencil portrait of *Madame A. Eyraud-Vaillant* by Modigliani for £1,000; a Pissarro, the water-colour, *Paysage d'Eragny*, £1,100; the *Tête Mysterieuse* by Odilon Redon for £1,100; *Poissons*, a water-colour by the same artist, £1,700; *Le Phare de Honfleur*, crayon conté with gouache, by Seurat, £5,000; and the *Jeune fille assise (la sœur de l'artiste)*, brush and ink, by Vuillard for £4,400.

In an evening sale on the same day forty-nine bronzes by Matisse, bought directly from the artist by Mr & Mrs Ahrenberg of Stockholm, sold for a total of £109,600, the highest price being £11,000 for a seated nude. Some had previously been exhibited at the Tate Gallery in London, and in Ottawa. The *Deux Negresses*, the only bronze group by Matisse known, was bought for £5,200.

On 8th July Sotheby sold works of art which included a very important Limoges enamel plaque of the Crucifixion—this realised £1,900; a singing-bird cage, early

19th-century by Les Frères Rochat, with a clock in the octagonal base, £920; and a Fabergé gold and diamond box, £2,000. A silver and hardstone chess-set, also by Fabergé, made £1,500.

Two important items of silver were sold by Christie's on 11th July. The first, a George II two-handled cup and cover in rococo style by Paul de Lamerie of 1742, weight 68 oz., sold for £1,500, whilst a Queen Anne plain two-handled cup with a coat of Arms, by Augustine Courtauld, weight 39 oz., of 1713, realized £520.

Christie's held a sale of antiquities on 12th July which included a good Benin bronze head of a princess, 13½″ in height, and probably of the 17th century. This was sold for £262. A Mexican marble mask, carved in high relief, with open mouth, belonging to the Olmec Culture—3rd–1st century B.C.—realised £126. A gold bracelet of square cross-section, 2¾″ in diameter and weighing almost 5 oz., in the form of a sinistral spiral, sold for £136. The provenance was probably Irish of the first millennium B.C. A very rare Cycladic Pentelic marble human figure, from Paros, of the third millennium B.C., 9½″ in height, made £315, and a pair of Etruscan squatting lions in limestone, 13½″ high, with sharply carved manes, £110. An alabaster funerary head showing Hellenistic influence from Southern Arabia of the 1st century B.C. realised £147, and a veined alabaster funerary frieze, also from Southern Arabia, and carved with ibex heads, £315.

On 12th July, in a mixed sale, Sotheby sold a number of early celadons belonging to the late Charles Russell. A very rare *tobi seiji*, or 'buckwheat' celadon vase of the Sung dynasty (960–1279), shown at the Oriental Ceramic Society's Exhibition of 1947, sold for £400, and a Ming Kuangtung shrine of characteristic form, much finer than most specimens of the kind, realised £100. £290 was paid for a rather late Lung Ch'üan water-pot in the form of a fabulous monster with a bird's head, recalling some archaic bronzes and formerly in the Eumorfopoulos Collection, whilst a very rare lobed ewer with a *kinuta* glaze made £540. A large Lung Ch'üan dish, 14½″ in diameter, with a sharply moulded dragon, of the Sung/Yüan dynasty, realised £400, and one of the Sung dynasty with two moulded fishes, 8¾″ in diameter, £290. A bulb bowl, the shallow body supported by three bracket feet, was sold for £320, whilst £340 was paid for a Chekiang vase of pear shape, with angular handles and pendant rings. The well-known Lung Ch'üan vase, which has been illustrated on several occasions and shown at the Oriental Ceramic Society's 1947 Exhibition, was sold for £195, and a cylindrical *jardinière* on three feet of the same provenance made £500.

An extremely rare vase with a *kinuta* glaze, the neck encircled by a moulded dragon and the globular body with petal moulding, sold for £1,750, whilst the well-known Chekiang *mei ping* vase of early Ming date from the Palace Collection, Pekin, which is moulded round the body with peacocks and peonies, realised £900. A Northern celadon bowl, formerly in the Eumorfopoulos Collection, superbly carved with a lotus scroll in the interior, made £740. Another, which had been seen at Burlington House in 1935–1936, realised £1,200, and its companion, equally celebrated, £1,100.

The sale, one of the best for a long time, contained several other remarkable items, the most important being an extremely rare white Ming stem-cup decorated *an hua* in white slip on the exterior. This, from the Imperial Palace and Eumorfopoulos Collections, is the only known stem-cup of the reign of the Emperor T'ien Shun (1457–1464), and was sold for £2,600 against competition from the Rijksmuseum. A fine pair of parrots on mottled rockwork bases, enamelled on biscuit and 9¼″ in height, realised £800, and a well-painted jar and cover with four evenly-spaced figures of women in *famille verte* enamels made £500. A pair of brilliantly enamelled *rouleau* vases in the same palette were sold for £750, whilst an unusual saucer-dish of Ming porcelain with the mark of Hung Chih (1488–1505) enamelled in *famille verte* colours in the reign of K'ang Hsi (1662–1722) with a lady at a rockwork table, went at £240.

An early Kandinsky sold at Sotheby on 13th July for £5,500. It was a winter landscape painted in 1908. A view of Murnau, also of 1908, by the same artist, realised £3,800. *A Woman with a Mandoline* of Juan Gris, painted in 1925, sold for £4,100; a Cubist still-life by Malevich for £1,800; a Degas, a sketch for the *Modiste garnissant au chapeau*, in pastel, £2,500; the *Normandy Horse* of Delacroix for £500; and studies of a mother and child in water-colour by Henry Moore, £320.

In a silver sale on the following day, in the same sale-room, a pair of superb George II cake-baskets (203 oz.) by Paul de Lamerie sold for £3,600; a set of three casters (49 oz.) by the same maker, £820; and a soup ladle for £250. A James II flagon (67 oz.) realised £1,250; a set of four George III oval sauce-tureens by Paul Storr (127 oz.), £780; and a Swedish marriage tankard, £440. A set of thirteen Apostle spoons of the early part of the 17th century sold for £900.

A sale of old Master pictures and drawings at Christie's on 15th July was well attended, and excellent prices were realised. Three *gouache* drawings of Roman scenes (*Capricci*—that is to say, topographical scenes with a quality of fantasy) made £525, £315, and £315 respectively. A Rowlandson, *Outside the Post House at Looen, near Ghent*, in pen, ink, and water-colour, realised £126.

Among the pictures, *Launching a Man o'War at Deptford* by John Clevely the Elder made £1,155, and an *Italian Coast Scene* by Charles F. Lacroix of Marseilles, £1,260. *Esther, Ahasuerus and Haman* by Jan Victors sold for £630, and a pair of panels by Vinckeboons, *Wooded River Landscape* and a *Wooded Village Landscape* together made £945. The *Flight into Egypt* of Simone Cantarini, was sold for £682, and another Rowlandson, a *View at Richmond* in pen, brown ink and water-colour, for £504.

A *Portrait of a Woman* by Van Dyck, a companion to a picture in the Musée Royale des Beaux Arts, Antwerp, sold for £6,300, whilst a portrait of the third Earl of Pembroke later in the sale made £115.

The most notable item was *The Entombment* of Le Nain, attributed to Mathieu for the usual reasons. This superb painting was sold for £6,090. It had previously been sold in 1863 for £6 18s. at a time when collectors made the acquisition of old Master paintings a poor second to that of Victorian sentimental rubbish.

A *Madonna and Child* by Francesco di Gentile da Fabriano realised £945, and four portraits by Louis Leopold Boilly sold for excellent prices: a *Portrait of the Artist* for £1,155; a *Portrait of Madame Chenard*, for £504; a *Portrait of Mademoiselle Gerar* at £1,995; and a *Portrait of a Young Woman* at £1,575. Two paintings by Cuyp, *Portrait of a Boy* and *Portrait of a Girl*, sold for £735 and £1,050 respectively, and a

Venus and Cupid of Boucher, signed, in black chalk heightened with white on grey-blue paper, for £168. The *Capture of Nancy* of Jacques Callot, in gold on black, a panel, sold for £105.

Other Italian paintings in the same sale included an Uccello, *The Resurrection*, on panel, at £735; a Bronzino, *Portrait of a Woman*, at £504; and a Guardi, *Capriccio of a Ruin with Labourers*, at £1,470.

On 18th July Sotheby sold Japanese colour-prints, drawings, and works of art, and an increase in interest on the part of buyers was noticeable. Three small ivory Shibayama vases fetched £160.

Sotheby continued the sale of the Greener collection of firearms on 25th July. An American Colt revolving rifle, first model, made £480; a pair of Pauly target pistols, £240; a Saxon wheel-lock pistol, dated 1591, £240; a breech-loading, seven-barrelled volley gun, bought for the Tower of London Armouries, £400; and a flint-lock sporting gun by Robert Wood of Birmingham, £260.

On 26th July Sotheby sold Chinese works of art, the most important object in the sale being a fine Ming jade reclining buffalo which was sold for £6,000, a little more than four times the price realised at its last appearance in the sale-room in 1949. A Ch'ien Lung grey jade carving of a water-buffalo and a boy, $6\frac{1}{4}''$ long, went for £1,200. A bowl painted in the rare underglaze copper red, probably Yüan dynasty, at one time in the Eumorfopoulos Collection, sold for £450, and a good *blanc-de-chine* figure of Kuan Yin for £200. A *famille rose* dinner service of 86 pieces went for £925, and a pair of Jesuit plates, 9″ diameter, £140.

In a picture sale on the following day a drawing of a harvesting scene heightened with body colour, by Samuel Palmer, sold for £490, and two Turner vignettes for £300 apiece.

At the Dorotheum on 13th September more than a thousand lots were sold. An oil on canvas of Friedrich von Amerling (1803–1887) *Caritas*, sold for Sch. 60,000 (£812); *Die neue Zofe* of Isidor Kaufmann (1853–1921), signed, for Sch. 40,000 (£542); *Vor der Schenke* by Theobald Michau, Sch. 32,000 (£432); *Moses schlägt Wasser aus dem Felsen*, by Cornelius van Poelenburg, Sch. 35,000 (£475); the *Hirtenmädchen aus der Campagna*, signed, by Anton Romako (1832–1889), for Sch. 35,000 (£475); *Die Kartenspieler*, by Gerard Seghers, Sch. 25,000 (£338); *Die spanischen Soldaten und die Bauern*, panel, by David Vinckeboons, Sch. 30,000 (£402); a standing monk, a drawing by Goya, Sch. 22,000 (£298); and, of the modern French school, a *Landschaft in Südfrankreich*, by Guillaumin, signed, Sch. 32,000 (£434).

A St John in carved limewood, part of a crucifixion, with the original colouring, from Bavaria, sold for Sch. 35,000 (£475); and a Gothic relief of the Birth of Christ, South German, early 16th century, with the original colours and gilding, for Sch. 25,000 (£338). A Dutch vitrine in the Louis Seize style, of walnut with a marquetry of flowers and plants, sold for Sch. 38,000 (£516).

On 12th October Sotheby sold the largest number of paintings by Picasso ever to be brought into a single sale. These had previously been on exhibition at the Tate Gallery, and were the property of Jacques Sarlie of New York. This began well with £4,000 for *Deux Femmes Marchant, des fiacres au Fond* of Picasso, in coloured chalk, signed.

His impressive *Femme Accroupie* realised £48,000, and *Nu* (*La Gommeuse*), £30,000. The *Femme assise dans un fauteuil* made £5,500; *L'homme au gant rouge*, £26,000; *Nature morte aux épis*, £9,000; *Nature morte à la bougie*, £17,000; and *Nature morte: vase de fleurs et plats de fruit sur une table*, £20,000.

A Braque, *La Femme au Miroir*, was sold for £42,000; and a Juan Gris, *Nature morte avec flacon, livre, et une pipe* for £5,000. There were a number of Modiglianis. Two oils on canvas, *Portrait du sculpteur Oscar Miestchaninoff* sold for £38,000, and another, of Madame Lunia Czechowska for £22,000. The *Profile de Femme* ('*La fille du cirque*') of Rouault made £9,000, and a Chaim Soutine, *L'Homme aux rubans*, £14,000.

On 18th October Sotheby began the sale of the Kitson Collection of Oriental works of art, the second part of which appeared in February, 1961. This remarkably fine collection attracted considerable attention, and prices were correspondingly good.

A set of eight rare amber carvings of the Eight Taoist Immortals sold for £520, and a boulder carving of the same period, 8″ high, made £160. These belonged to the period of the Emperor Ch'ien Lung (1736–1795). A large Imperial peach bowl, superbly carved, sold for £400. An early brush-washer of the Sung-Yüan dynasty carved in the form of a lotus with four lizards realised £240.

Cinnabar lacquer, mostly of the Ch'ien Lung period, sold well. A large rectangular panel carved with the Taoist Paradise, with Immortals and the Heavenly Pavilion, realised £500. The *cloisonné* enamel was of a quality rarely seen in the sale-room, and a pair of beakers in the form of bronze *ku*, with two *t'ao t'ieh* masks, of the Ch'ien Lung period sold for £210. A large pair of Imperial vases, 33″ high, with lobed globular bodies and trumpet necks, formerly in the Yuan Ming Yuan Palace, Pekin, realised £550, and a massive double peach bowl, 29″ long, enamelled with various emblems on a pale blue ground, £700. The latter appeared in the Exhibition of Chinese Art at Burlington House. A Ming cup and stand with the mark of Hsüan-tê realised £360, and £340 was paid for a dish of mid-16th-century dating. These had been included in the Oriental Ceramic Society's Ming Exhibition of 1957. Another Ming example, a 16th-century pear-shaped bottle with dragon handles realised £200.

The highest prices were paid for an Imperial altar-set of the Ch'ien Lung period which comprised a pair of pricket candlesticks supported on the back of a recumbent ram, and a pair of stands of the same form, each ram with a man seated on its back, at £1,550; and a pair of recumbent buffaloes in white *cloisonné* with the hooves, horns, and muzzle in gilt metal, the details of the ears, mouth, and nostrils picked out in red, and the eyes in black, at £1,250. The first had been exhibited at Burlington House in 1935–1936.

The jade was of exceptional quality, although all of it belonged to the Ch'ing dynasty. £620 was paid for a pale green libation cup in the form of a rhinoceros horn, finely carved and pierced and with a long inscription; £680 for a *koro* and cover with a continuous design of *t'ao t'ieh* masks, the colour of sodden snow; £580 for a superb cloud-white lotus bowl carved with overlapping petals; and £720 for a group of a lotus with a small crane—a magnificent composition in light green jade.

A remarkable brush-pot in grey-green jade, carved with Shou Lao and two Immortals in the Taoist Paradise, sold for £2,400; a large, extremely translucent bowl of mutton-fat jade, carved with longevity characters and the Eight Happy Omens, for £1,600; and a superb cylindrical brush-holder, deeply carved with a continuous mountain landscape, in jade of the much-sought spinach-green colour, for £5,000.

The second of the important Autumn dispersals of modern art was held by the Parke-Bernet Galleries on 26th October, 1960. It included works sent by Mrs Gladys Lloyd Robinson, at one time co-owner of the well-known Edward G. Robinson Collection. Prices reached familiar levels for works of this character.

A drawing by Vuillard of about 1895, *Le malade imaginaire*, sold for $3,500 (£1,250), whilst a Boudin *Beach Scene*, in pencil and water-colour, made $5,250 (£1,875). A Chinese ink drawing, *Haitian Woman*, by Matisse, and a *Balleteuse*, in black crayon on buff paper, by Degas, realised $2,250 (£803) and $3,250 (£1,160) respectively.

An Epstein bronze, *Kathleen*, was sold for $3,500 (£1,250), but the highest price for sculpture was reserved for the *Two Penguins*, in white marble, of Brancusi. This, $32,500 (£11,602), was governed to some extent by the fact that only two or three examples of his work are now ever likely to be for sale.

A Boudin, *Boats at Dieppe*, sold for $14,000 (£4,998). A Vlaminck, *Paysage (Rue de Village)*, realised $10,000 (£3,570), whilst $22,000 (£7,854) was given for his *Hotel du Laboureur, Rueil-la-Gadelière*. Modigliani was represented in the sale by *Boy in a Green Suit* at $57,500 (£20,627). A Pissarro, *Avant Port de Dieppe*, changed hands at $35,000 (£12,495), whilst the highest price of the sale, $65,000 (£23,205) was realised by the Degas, *Trois Jockeys*, sent by a New York private collector. This had, at one time, been in the possession of Ambrose Vollard, and had passed through the hands of Durand Ruel.

A Vuillard pastel, *Interior with family scene*, possessed the best conceivable pedigree, since it was a portrait of Mr & Mrs Robinson and their son, executed in the Paris Hôtel Plaza Athénée in 1939. It was sold for $12,000 (£4,284). The much-illustrated *Potentate: Pierrot* of Rouault realised $35,000 (£12,495).

The last lots were devoted to the work of contemporary French, Italian, and American artists. Of these, only *La Bohémienne* of Luigi Corbellini ($1,000—£357) and the *Jockey* of Gabriel Dauchot ($1,100—£393) achieved four figures in dollars.

On 27th October, in a sale of furniture at Christie's, a Sheraton satinwood writing-table made £1,155, and a satinwood marquetry commode, £1,470. A small Pembroke table sold for £504; a satinwood writing-table for £378; a Regency bookcase in the manner of Charles Hope for £609; and a Chippendale mahogany kettle-stand for £409.

Sotheby's sale of English and Continental ceramics of 8th November opened with a number of lots of decorative Continental *maiolica* and *faïence*. Four 17th-century Montelupo dishes, decorated typically in bright colours, sold well at £35, £58, £58, and £56. These were excellent prices for such late work. A Castel Durante dish, dated 1588, which was also late, realised £42, and a Faenza drug jar of about 1530, £65. These prices suggest that a sale of important *maiolica* might show some distinct advances. A Marseilles dish painted with ladies in a terraced garden from the Fauchier factory (*c.* 1750) sold for £75, and a good Niderviller figure of a peasant for £48. A Castelli plaque, painted and signed by Francesco Grue, of St Jerome made £60 despite the subject; another by the same hand, but with a secular subject, realised £85 later in the sale. A pair of plaques with scenes representing Earth and Air from the Elements after Amiconi made £170, and a dish attractively painted with a cavalier on a horse, probably from Talavera, £30.

The remainder of the sale was devoted to porcelain. The work of Swansea made excellent prices, a pair of shaped plates from the Dynevor Service, painted by David Evans, selling for £190, an oval dish from the same service for £100, and a square dish for £130. A Worcester yellow ground basket, cover, and stand, of the type recorded in discussing the sale of 10th May, sold for £360, and an even finer blue scale specimen immediately following for £430. A remarkable Chamberlain's Worcester jug, painted by Humphrey Chamberlain with a scene of huntsmen carousing, with a lilac ground, made £360, whilst a pair of Spode vases, 6½" high, of the perennially popular 711 pattern, made £120.

A pair of Longton Hall leaf-dishes painted with bouquets by the 'Trembly Rose' painter went to £230, and a very rare, well-painted pair of shell salts from the same factory made £120. A rare early Bow figure of a huntress sold for £120; one of Spring, derived from the well-known Chelsea set of the Seasons which appeared later in the sale, for £190; and a Harlequin seated on a tree-trunk, after a Meissen original, for £170. A rare pair of a Gardner and Companion on high pierced bases of about 1758 sold for £330.

Four Chelsea figures of the Seasons, sold separately in successive lots, realised for Spring, £260; for Summer, £250; for Autumn, £190; and for Winter, £240—a considerable advance on the price realised in earlier sales for the same figures sold as a set. The result suggests that some collectors are willing to pay a higher price, proportionately, to make up existing incomplete sets.

The sale included some rare Chelsea miniature figures. These averaged about 2½" in height. A group of two putti sold for £48; a poet seated, writing in a book, £145; a pair of a gallant and his companion, £145; a highlander, £150; a gallant, his hat under his arm, £150; a gallant bowing, £150; two identical models of a hunter, £250 for the two; and a pair of a Shepherd and Shepherdess, £320. Most had a red anchor or a double red anchor mark.

Among the Continental porcelain was included a rare *bonbonnière* from Mennecy in the form of a sphinx. This, with silver mounts, sold for £240. A very attractive Vincennes vase, similar to a pair in the Chavagnac sale of 1911, was inexpensive at £400. A late pair of Frankenthal groups by Melchior, who arrived at the factory in 1779, sold for £150, and a white Nymphenburg figure of a pilgrim by Bustelli, £210. A good early pair of Meissen toilet jars painted in the Kakiemon style sold for £410; a Meissen kennel with two pug-dog puppies (despite repairs) for £160; a fine Meissen bowl, painted with Höroldt *chinoiseries* within a baroque scrollwork *cartouche*, £300; and another with a yellow ground, painted with river scenes, for £340.

A rare Böttger red stoneware sugar-box decorated with wheel-engraving and lacquer colours, apparently identical with the one sold on 26th April, made £160—an increase of £45 on the previous price.

An important five-day sale which realised a total of almost \$958,250 (£342,273) was held by the Parke-Bernet Galleries in New York early in November, by order of the Myron and Anabel Taylor Foundation. The late Myron C. Taylor was Presidential envoy to the Vatican from 1929 until 1950, and a former chairman of the United States Steel Corporation. This was a collection which recalled those of the 1890s and the first decades of the twentieth century. Taste in the mid-twentieth century has removed a little from Renaissance magnificence, and this provided an excellent opportunity to see what the demand for important things of the period would be. Expectedly some prices were lower than they would have been before 1930, making due allowance for the intervening devaluation of currency, but they were often distinctly higher than market conditions have suggested hitherto. The more important things, in fact, sold well. There were also many things of a kind much in demand today, as will be seen from some of the prices quoted below.

The first part of the sale included such furniture as a good Tudor Nonesuch marquetry chest which was cheap at $500 (£179), and a James I carved three-tiered buffet was sold for the same price. A set of seven Queen Anne side-chairs in walnut, upholstered in needlepoint, made $1,750 (£624), whilst a fine George I settee with a double chair-back and ball and claw feet—a remarkably elegant specimen—went for $1,500 (£536).

A set of six graceful armchairs in Chippendale's Chinese style with needlepoint seats made $10,500 (£3,748), whilst six side-chairs *en suite*, but with upholstered backs in needlepoint worked with mythological scenes, the seats with Aesop's Fables, realised $4,800 (£1,714), a total of $15,300 (£5,462) for the twelve.

A large Coromandel screen, 9′ in height and opening to 19′, was sold for $5,000 (£1,784), whilst another, even larger, was sold later in the sale for $6,750 (£2,409).

The most important items, and the largest prices, were reserved for the sessions of 11th and 12th November. In this part was included French and Italian furniture of the 16th century to the 18th, Gothic and Renaissance sculpture, and eleven important Gothic tapestries.

A pair of carved and gilded German *tabourets* of mid-18th century in the style of Louis Quinze were sold for $4,200 (£1,500) A pair of Louis Seize carved and gilded *fauteuils* with polychrome decoration, made by Louis Falconet who worked between 1738 and 1750, realised $5,500 (£1,963), and a *canapé* decorated in the same way, and also upholstered in embroidered yellow satin, made by Nicolas-Quinibert Foliot, went to $10,500 (£3,748). These came originally from the collection of the Duchesse de Montmorency.

An unusual beginning to the last day's sale was an Egyptian bronze hawk of the XXVth dynasty, $8\frac{1}{4}″$ in height, at $2,250 (£803); a fragment of an Assyrian marble bas-relief of the 9th century, which was excavated by Layard on the site of the Palace of Ashurnasipal II, $4,500 (£1,607); and a good marble lion, 36″ long, of the 4th century from Greece, which sold for $2,500 (£893).

A 16th-century limestone head of St Sylvester (School of Rheims), wearing a high triple crown, picked out in scarlet and gold, realised $5,750 (£2,052), whilst a distinguished portrait bust of a young woman in wood, with traces of polychrome decoration, went for $3,000 (£1,071). Another Gothic sculpture, a relief depicting the three Magi of 15th-century Flemish workmanship, also sold for $3,000 (£1,071).

An attractive limestone statuette of St Catherine from 15th-century France, 41″ in height, made $5,500 (£1,250), and an altar-piece in three parts from Spain of the same period, formerly in the Cloister of Poblet near Barcelona, and depicting eight Cistercian monks, sold for $16,000 (£5,712).

The highest price of the sale, $40,000 (£14,280), was reserved for the following lot, a glazed terracotta lunette by Andrea della Robbia in white against a blue background, originally in the collection of Count Benevento Pasalini dall'Onda. This fine Florentine piece depicts the Angel Gabriel holding in one hand a sword, and in the other scales with two human souls in the balance.

Among the pictures the *Isola S. Giorgio Maggiore, Venice* of Guardi was bought for $10,550 (£3,748) and the S. Catherine of Alexandra by Luini for $4,500 (£1,607).

An interesting portrait of the Emperor Maximilian I of Germany, a contemporary replica of the Dürer portrait in the Kunsthistorisches Museum of Vienna, was sold for $1,700 (£607). A very similar replica of this portrait was sold by the Galerie Charpentier in Paris on 14th June, 1960, for 31,000 francs (£2,518).

Two Florentine *cassone* panels, *The Triumph of L. Aemilius Paulus over the Persians* by the Anghiari Master, a contemporary of Uccello, and the unattributed *Arrival and Triumph of a Prince* were sold for $8,000 (£2,856) and $9,000 (£3,213) respectively, whilst a 15th-century Spanish altar-piece of six panels, depicting the legend of St Michael and Galgano, realised $10,000 (£3,570).

Among the Renaissance and baroque furniture, a carved walnut and chestnut table of 16th-century Spanish workmanship sold for $1,000 (£357), and a richly carved Florentine *credenza* of the same period for $900 (£321). A good Tuscan octagonal table, with four dolphins forming a cruciform centre support, fetched $800 (£286). Even a superbly carved armorial *credenza*, Sienese of the 16th century, only realised $1,100 (£393), and a remarkable pair of Florentine *stipi á Bambocci* of the same period, $750 (£268) and $700 (£250) respectively. Furniture of this kind was undoubtedly undervalued by the bidders present, and, at the prices, is a worthwhile speculation for the future.

Of the tapestries, a *millefleurs* example with animals of about 1510 made $17,500 (£6,248); a slightly earlier armorial tapestry, bought by the Metropolitan Museum, $32,500 (£11,603); a Brussels tapestry of about 1500 depicting *Esther before Ahasuerus*, $9,000 (£3,213); and another, slightly later, of Tyndareus, King of Sparta, $12,500 (£4,463). The three Touraine tapestries of about 1515, representing the *Marriage of Peace and Love*, the *Triumph of Virtue*, and the *Marriage of Tobias and Sara*, made $7,000 (£2,500), $16,000 (£5,712), and $5,000 (£1,784), respectively.

A number of fine Persian carpets were included in the sale. A rare medallion carpet of the 16th century from north-west Persia, 20′ 8″ × 7′ 10″ realised $8,000 (£2,856). This had an apple-green ground. A fine and equally rare Hispano-Arab carpet of the late 17th century, 22′ 10″ × 15′ 6″, realised $4,500 (£1,606), whilst the highest price, $9,000 (£3,213), was reserved for a magnificent late 16th-century hunting carpet from north-west Persia, measuring 14′ 2″ × 7′ 9″.

At Sotheby on the 11th November an engraved Jacobite decanter sold for £145, and a wine-glass with an engraved portrait of Prince Charles Edward for £230. Another portrait glass sold for £160.

In a sale of English and Continental porcelain at Christie's on 14th November a pair of Bow figures of a Bull and a Cow sold for £126; a rare Chelsea figure of a Guan, taken from Edwards' *Natural History of Uncommon Birds*, raised red anchor mark, for £735; and a small pair of brightly-coloured birds from Bow, £441. A tea-bowl and saucer with *chinoiserie* figures and a blue scale ground from Worcester, from the Bodenham service, brought £155; and a handsome dessert service of 35 pieces, split into lots, painted with exotic birds in river landscapes, from the same factory, a total of £1,449. A rare Chelsea group of the *Tyrolese Dancers* after the Eberlein model made £273; a pair of du Paquier Vienna pilgrim-vases, painted in *Schwarzlot* with mythological subjects, £1,102; a good Chelsea figure of *La Nourrice* after the Avon model of Barthélémy Blenod, £609; a gold anchor marked figure of the Imperial Shepherdess, 13″ high and incised with an R, £199; a set of three Sèvres vases painted by Rosset with harbour scenes, and having an *œil de perdrix* pattern on the ground, £630; a Meissen spirit barrel modelled by Gottfried Müller, the barrel painted with harbour scenes, £588; a good pair of a Chinaman and companion seated, by Eberlein, £399; two Nymphenburg *chinoiserie* figures, by Bustelli, on typical rococo bases, £1,995; a pair of Frankenthal figures, by J. F. Lück, of the Merchant and his wife, £231; another pair by the same hand of a Lady and Gentleman, £252; an important pair of Sèvres vases, with *bleu de roi* ground and shipping scenes by Morin, £1,102; and a Meissen Oriental lady, by Kändler and Reinicke, for £273.

At Christie's on 15th November £840 was paid for a pair of Louis Quatorze ewers in tortoiseshell, and £714 for a casket with the Arms of Charles II of Spain. A silver mounted nautilus shell, engraved with mythological scenes, realised £420; an English agate and gold snuff box, *c.* 1730, £283; and a French gold-mounted box inset with a portrait of Mademoiselle de la Vallière, by Petitot, £231.

At Sotheby on the following day a portrait of the Duke of Sussex of 1793, by Louis Gauffier, sold for £1,150; a van Goyen landscape for £1,050; a still-life by de Heem for £1,000; and a flower-piece by Blain de Fontenoy for £1,600.

On 17th November Sotheby sold some important silver. A set of candlesticks, by Paul de Lamerie (88 oz.), realised £5,600; a silver-gilt sideboard ewer (79 oz.), by the same maker, £4,200; a pair of salvers (72 oz.), £3,000; an oval soup-tureen and cover, £3,400; and a coffee-pot of 1743, £1,800. Among work by other makers, a silver-gilt Monteith by Anthony Nelme sold for £1,100; a ewer by 1696 by David Willaume for £1,300; and an Italian silver-gilt enamelled chalice of the 15th century, £1,000. £2,000 was given for a Charles II toilet-set; £1,300 for a coffee-pot by Humphrey Payne of 1718; £2,500 for a seven-sided teapot by Isaac Ribouleau; and £1,500 for a Charles II octagonal casket engraved with *chinoiseries*. A standing salt of the early 17th century made £3,400.

Several small pictures by Constable were sold in Christie's sale-room on the following day. *A Suffolk Copse*, of 1809, realised £2,100; *A Stormy Sky at Hampstead*, £2,100; a *Landscape with Shepherd and Sheep*, £1,575; and a *Landscape with a Cloudy Sky*, £2,520. The *Piping Shepherd* by Reynolds was bought for £1,365; a race-horse, *Whisker*, by Herring, £840; *Flying Dutchman with Charles Marlow up*, by the same hand,

£1,732; a pair of hunting pictures by Sartorius, £1,155; a racing picture by Munnings, £997; and a landscape attributed to Paul Sandby, £2,100.

On 22nd November Christie's sold armour from the Metropolitan Museum, New York. A good Swiss dagger of about 1550 was bought for £231; an Italian parade shield of wood and embossed leather for £220; and a German suit in the style of the late 15th century for £205. An English three-quarter suit was acquired for £294, and an Italian armet, of about 1575, for £147. At Sotheby, in a sale of Japanese works of art, a *kakemono* by Hokusai was sold for £280.

Some important items were included in a sale of modern paintings at Sotheby on 24th November. It was particularly notable for the rare appearance of a work by *le douanier* Rousseau, *The Football Players*, which sold for £37,000—perhaps a little less than anticipated. A Rouault gouache of *Le Palais d'Ubu Roi* sold for £14,000; the *Nu debout dans l'eau* of Renoir, 1888, for £38,000; *Westminster*, of 1900, by Dérain, £3,800; Modigliani's *Boy with Red Hair*, £21,000; the Gauguin, *Femme Assise à l'ombre des Palmiers*, for £38,000; a Cézanne, *La Maison Abandonnée au Tholonet*, for £38,000; a Monet of water lilies at Giverny, originally bought from Durand Ruel, for £18,000; a *Reclining Nude* of 1890, by Renoir, for £16,000; *Harlequin with a guitar* by Juan Gris, of 1925, £16,000; a *Nature Morte* by Nicolas de Stael, of 1952, for £13,000; and a set of thirteen water-colours, by Dufy, £19,000.

On the following day a Salomon van Ruysdael, *An Estuary*, of 1651, sold at Christie's for £9,450, and a *View of the Grand Canal, Venice*, attributed to Canaletto, for £3,570. A van Dyck, *Jan Malderus, Bishop of Antwerp*, realised £2,520; a *Young Girl*, of 1770, by Drouais, £2,205, and a companion picture by the same hand for £2,100.

At Sotheby a pair of Adam marquetry card-tables sold for £1,000, and a good pair of mahogany Pembroke tables for £600.

On 17th March Christie's established a record for the total of a single day's sale of French furniture, and then broke it in the same year on 24th November. The lots in both sales were the property of a number of owners.

A good price (£840) was paid early in the sale for a large pair of Bavarian figures of saints, carved in limewood in the early part of the 18th century by an unknown hand. This suggests a renewal of interest in early wood-carving. Earlier in the year a group of three saints by Tilmann Riemenschneider carved at the beginning of the 16th century made £6,200 at Sotheby, and four figures of Christ and three Apostles were sold in Vienna at the Dorotheum in the March sale for 100,000 schillings (£1,425). In November a Gothic portrait bust of 16th century in wood from France made £1,050 in New York. The higher price for the Riemenschneider group is partly accounted for by its quality, but he was also an outstanding carver of his time.

The interest in ormolu of all kinds, to be noticed in sales throughout the year, can be seen in the prices paid for such things as Louis Quinze wall-lights, a set of four with foliage back-plates, each bearing five lights, the ormolu nozzles of rococo vase form, making £714. A pair of *chenets* modelled as dragons, of the same period, made £441. An important pair of Louis Quinze candelabra of ormolu and Sèvres porcelain, finely chased and enriched with porcelain flowers, sold for £3,150; another pair of ormolu wall-lights, with porcelain flower enrichment, for £2,835; and still another pair of wall-lights, with standing figures of Columbine and a youth in trellised arbours of ormolu, £1,837. The following pair of candelabra, also enriched with porcelain flowers, made £2,520. Decorative Italian bronzes included a bronze and parcel-gilt *chinoiserie* figure of the 17th century, $11\frac{1}{2}''$ high, which made £714; whilst a pair of mythological groups of Jupiter and Apollo, both with the infant Hercules, on *rouge* marble pedestals sold for £525.

The increasing interest in French furniture of the 19th century, noticeable throughout the year, was evident in the price realised by a bronze and ormolu side-table made about 1864 in the tradition of the 18th-century *ébénistes* by Jules Dalou. This was sold for £1,995.

A set of Louis Seize chairs, painted and partly gilt on a cream ground, with carved enrichments and a Beauvais tapestry covering, made £2,835. Two Louis Seize parquetry *consoles-dessertes*, one stamped J. H. Riesener, were sold for £3,780; and a Louis Quinze marquetry table with a superb inlay, representing the tesselated courtyard of a palace, returned to Paris at £2,835. The highest price of the day, £18,375, was given by a Paris dealer for an elegant Louis Quinze commode decorated with flowers and foliage in gold and colours over a ground of *vernis Martin*. A commode of black lacquer of the same period was bought for Paris at £6,300.

A remarkably fine Louis Seize marquetry commode by David Roentgen, superbly inlaid with *chinoiserie* designs recalling those of Höroldt, realised £9,975.

Christie's sold a pair of Ch'ien Lung figures of hawks decorated in *famille rose* colours, on Louis Seize ormolu bases, for £7,560 on 28th November, and a very rare pair of Japanese figures from Arita, of a stag and a doe, late 17th century, made £1,155. At Sotheby on the following day a pair of Chelsea gold anchor period groups of the Seasons realised £980; a Bow Italian Comedy figure of Scaramouche, £700; and a Worcester scale-yellow chocolate cup and saucer, £600.

A sale of paperweights at Sotheby on 28th November, 1960, testified to the popularity of these among collectors. This notable dispersal was the property of the late Colonel M. Robert Guggenheim of Washington, D.C.

A fine St Louis pink encased overlay weight realised £700; and an important green overlay moulded salamander weight from the same source, £750. £190 was paid for a St Louis crown weight, and £200 for another of the same kind. A close *millefiore* weight from Baccarat, dated 1848, made £180; and a scattered *millefiore* weight of the same date, £150.

£210 was paid for a Baccarat portrait weight of Queen Victoria; £190 for a St Louis mushroom weight, inscribed *SL 1848*; £260 for a very rare St Louis carpet ground weight, dated 1848; and £175 for another with an animal silhouette. A St Louis grapevine weight made £165; a Baccarat pear weight, £160; a Baccarat yellow flower weight, £115; and a rare St. Louis flower weight, £150.

A Clichy flat bouquet weight realised £210; a large rare St Louis weight similarly decorated, £260; and a similar Baccarat weight, £310. A Baccarat green flash overlay weight was sold for £225; a Clichy turquoise double overlay weight, £440; and a Baccarat snake paperweight, £340.

At Sotheby on 30th November prices were high for good English painting. *North*

Country Mails at the Peacock, Islington, by James Pollard, was bought for £19,000; a Samuel Palmer, *The Weald of Kent,* for £6,000; and a shooting party in a winter landscape, of 1806, by James Ward, for £4,800. A Constable, *Country Road, Dedham,* made £2,100, and the *Old Barn,* £4,800. Turner's *Llanthony Abbey,* of about 1834, sold for £5,000, and his *Aske Hall, Yorkshire* for £3,200.

Constable's portrait of Anne Mary Constable sold for £5,200; a Gainsborough portrait of Dr Marsh for £2,400; one of the actress, Fanny Kemble, of 1834, by Sully, for £2,500; and one of Sir Edward Every by Romney for £2,800.

Bonington's *Château of the Duchesse de Berri on the Garonne* was bought for £6,800.

On the same day silver was sold at Christie's, a patten and chalice of about 1530 being bought for £5,000. The Great Seal of Ireland cup and cover, of 1593, was acquired by the Belfast City Art Gallery, with the aid of the National Art Collections Fund, for £7,000. A teapot, stand, and lamp, by John Leach, of 1709 (34 oz.) realised £2,000; one of 1714 (16 oz.), by Simon Pantin, £1,400; and an octagonal coffee-pot of 1711, by John Folkingham, 27 oz., for £800.

On the next day Sotheby sold a Queen Anne two-handled cup and cover by Johan Clifton (52 oz.) for £2,500; and a George II oval soup-tureen and cover (96 oz.) by Charles Kandler, with the crest and cipher of William IV, for £1,600. A Norwegian peg tankard of about 1690, by Michael Olsen of Bergen (72 oz.), went for £1,450; a coffee-pot by Heinrich Wittkopf of Stockholm (33 oz.) for £1,400; and a pair of Austrian soup-tureens of 1781 (345 oz.) by J. S. Wurth for £1,300.

On 2nd December a pair of small flower paintings by Fantin-Latour sold at Christie's for £5,880, whilst £540 was paid for a Brussels tapestry at Sotheby, and a similar sum for a small Kashan silk carpet.

On 5th December Sotheby sold a rare mid-16th-century South German pendant, for £5,800, and a vase in gold, enamel, and jasper by J. V. Morel, of 1855, with the motto of the Hope family, for £5,000. A 16th-century South German jewelled and enamel pendant in the form of a pelican brought £2,400, and a Spanish gold and emerald pendant as a dragon, *c.* 1580, £1,100. A bowenite and rose diamond Easter egg by Fabergé made £2,400; a *bonbonnière* in the form of a Doge's cap, £1,350 and a gold box, inset with a miniature by Grabelot, £1,550. A Louis Quinze gold and lacquer snuff-box of 1752 realised £2,750; one of gold, enamel and diamonds, of 1760, £2,800; and one of gold chased with an ornament of gardening tools for £3,200. An important Battersea enamel casket painted with designs after Watteau and Boucher was bought for £1,700.

The well-known collection of Chinese works of art, the property of Mme L. Wannieck, was sold at the Palais Galliéra and the Hôtel Drouot on 2nd and 5th December. M. Leon Wannieck travelled much in China, and made important gifts to the Paris Museums, including the Musée Guimet. An important Ming *potiche* of the *san ts'ai* type in deep blue, turquoise, and yellow, with a design of peonies, sold for NF. 10,000 (£5,729); and another, also decorated in *san ts'ai* enamels, with dragon handles, NF. 12,000 (£875). Of the K'ang Hsi wares, two Lions of Fo, one playing with a ball, the other with cubs, aubergine and turquoise blue enamel on *biscuit,* realised NF. 5,000

(£365); a baluster vase, turquoise blue enamel on *biscuit*, engraved with *t'ao t'ieh* masks, NF. 5,800 (£423); two matching turquoise blue bowls, NF. 6,500 (£473); two kylins in turquoise blue, NF. 13,500 (£984); a joss-stick holder in the form of a toad in turquoise blue, NF. 16,000 (£1,136); two parrots on a rock, the birds in blue, the rocks aubergine, with iron-red beaks and feet, NF. 43,000 (£3,135); a flat bowl in the form of the peach of longevity, turquoise blue, NF. 8,300 (£604); a flat bowl in the form of an aquatic leaf, in turquoise blue and aubergine, NF. 5,800 (£423); an incense burner in turquoise blue in the form of a human figure asleep on the back of a toad, NF. 18,000 (£1,313); a pair of important Lions of Fo in turquoise blue and aubergine, NF. 10,500 (£766); a figure of Pu-tai crouching and smiling, in turquoise blue, a joss-stick holder, NF. 12,000 (£875); a flat dish in the form of a water-lily leaf, with lotus flowers and a lizard round the edge, NF. 7,200 (£425); a covered box in the form of a conch shell, turquoise blue, NF. 9,000 (£656).

Polychrome porcelain of the same period included a seated cat in white porcelain decorated with brown in a floral style, the base with flowers in coloured enamels, NF. 6,300 (£460); a vase of *rouleau* shape with decoration in black enamel and gold, NF. 6200 (£452); a pair of *potiches*, covered with a mirror-black glaze decorated with floral motifs in gold, NF. 6,000 (£437); a pair of ewers in yellow, aubergine, and green, in the form of chickens, NF. 6,300 (£460); and an important group of Kuan Yin holding a child, standing on a fabulous monster, richly decorated in colours, NF. 8,000 (£582).

Belonging to the period of Yung Chêng were a pair of hawks on rocks, richly coloured in aubergine, blue, coral red, and blue, which realised NF. 17,500 (£1,276). Two cocks, each on a rock, of the period of Ch'ien Lung, decorated in colours, sold for NF. 41,000 (£2,989); a pair of hawks also decorated in rich colours, NF. 30,000 (£2,188); a pair of seated dogs, grey and white, NF. 8,800 (£640); a pair of ducks, painted in colours, NF. 21,000 (£1,531); a small pheasant on a rock, polychrome, NF. 52,000 (£3,642); a pair of hawks, also in polychrome, NF. 30,000 (£2,188); and an important pair of *potiches* decorated in *famille rose* colours, with reserves in European style, perhaps inspired by the Dutch artist, Pronck, NF. 103,000 (£7,510).

Pictures and furniture belonging to the late Prince Ali Khan were sold at the Palais Galliéra on 5th December, as well as the property of other collectors. The *Jeune Femme Assise* of Mary Cassatt sold for NF. 70,000 (£5,104); the *Marché aux Pommes* of Marquet for NF. 55,000 (£4,007); and a Vlaminck, *Le Pont*, for NF. 73,000 (£5,322).

A writing, or desk, chair in natural carved wood, upholstered in leather, period of Louis Quinze, sold for NF. 13,100 (£955); four armchairs in natural wood, carved and moulded (three, period of Louis Quinze, and the fourth in the style of that reign), NF. 8,800 (£636); a commode veneered with ebony and tortoiseshell marquetry, with serpentine marble top, stamped C. Cochois, early 18th century, NF. 30,500 (£2,224); a chest of seven drawers (*semainier*) veneered in rose and violet woods, period of Louis Quinze, stamp of A. Delorme, NF. 13,300 (£970); a lacquer commode decorated with *chinoiseries* and flowers on a yellow ground, period Louis Quinze, stamp of F. Reizell, some restoration, NF. 31,300 (£2,282); and a flat writing-desk, with ormolu mounts and a red leather top, veneered with violet wood, with the stamp of the celebrated

18th-century *ébéniste*, Peridiex le Père, NF. 17,300 (£2,296).

The sale by Sotheby of the collection of European porcelain belonging to the late Oscar Dusendschon of Geneva on 6th December invited comparison with the earlier dispersal of the first part of the Blohm Collection.

The demand for Chelsea scent-bottles and 'toys' continued unabated, and prices followed the same pattern as in the July sale. If anything, they were a trifle higher for the more important specimens. The figure of £1,700 for an exceptionally fine Meissen snuff-box surmounted by a small figure of a Mops, and painted in the manner of C. F. Herold, was the result of keen competition for an extremely important item.

Prices for French porcelain were, on the whole, a little lower than might have been expected. An extremely rare group from Vincennes, *Les Mangeurs de Raisins* after Boucher, made £2,100, but many of the remaining lots were lower than the general trend of the porcelain market for other things. A startling price was £3,600 paid for a Chelsea group of Tyrolese Dancers after a Meissen model by Eberlein. There are a number of Chelsea examples in existence, as well as at least one (in the Victoria & Albert Museum) modelled in China for export in the middle of the 18th century. Quality of this specimen was good, but the price must remain one of those sale-room mysteries for which there is no obvious explanation. In a previous sale at Christie's on 14th November, a similar group made £273 which, whilst it was a trifle low, was much more realistic.

Prices for good German porcelain maintained their earlier levels, although much of it was not comparable with specimens in the Blohm Collection either for rarity or quality. Three fine Höchst groups—*Der Bekränzte Schläfer*, *The Disturbed Slumber*, and a girl milking a goat, all in the manner of Melchior, made £380, £400, and £280 respectively. Two fine Meissen figures of cats on Louis Seize ormolu bases made £1,700; a pair of ormolu-mounted Meissen figures of Musicians, £1,150; an important Louis Quinze ormolu arbour with modelled flowers and a Meissen Italian Comedy Group inset, £2,000; a rare group by Kändler and Reinicke of a Sultan riding an elephant on a Louis Quinze ormolu base, £3,600; and a fine Louis Quinze ormolu clock by Charles le Roi with a group of peasant lovers, £3,200.

On 7th December the Palais Galliéra of Paris dispersed the important and well-known collection of 18th-century art assembled by Richard Penard y Fernandez.

L'Ara, a water-colour gouache, by J.-B. Hilaire, signed, sold for NF. 22,500 (£1,641); the *Fêtes à l'occasion de la naissance du Dauphin: Arrivée de la reine à l'hôtel de ville de Paris, 1782*, signed, pen and ink wash, and the *Feu d'Artifice, place de l'hôtel de ville de Paris, 1782*, signed, pen and ink wash heightened with white, of Moreau le Jeune for NF. 17,000 (£1,240). The *Académie de femme debout*, black crayon heightened with white, by Prud'hon, realised NF. 18,000 (£1,312); a pen and bistre wash, *Feuille d'etudes*, of Tiepolo, NF. 7,000 (£510); *L'Arrivée du Bac*, oil on panel, by Jean-Louis Demarne, NF. 31,000 (£2,260); *L'Heureux ménage*, circular canvas, inscribed on the reverse 'To the illustrious Sir Thomas Lawrence, the author of the only interesting method of portrait painting . . .', NF. 160,000 (£11,663); a *Portrait of Madame de Sevigné* by Pierre Mignard, NF. 52,000 (£3,791); the *Répétition dans le théâtre de verdure du château de Saint-Cloud, d'une fête donnée par Louis-Philippe d'Orléans* of Jean Pillement

NF. 31,000 (£2,260); and *Le chat favouri* of Jean-Frédéric Schmall, NF. 47,000 (£3,426).

Some remarkably fine silver included a ewer and stand in silver-gilt by Nicholas de Launay, of 1704, which realised NF. 145,000 (£10,573); a pair of oval plates of 1766, by François-Thomas Germain, NF. 20,000 (£1,456); a silver ewer of baluster form, by Philippe-Auguste Boursin, Paris, 1681, NF. 33,000 (£2,405); a pair of candlesticks of 1771, by Jacques-Nicolas Roettiers, made for the Russian Court (the Orloff service), NF. 40,000 (£2,916); and a bronze *torchère*, chiselled and gilded, after Delafosse, period of Louis Seize, NF. 13,000 (£948).

A white marble vase of ovoid form sculpted with *amoretti*, and attributed to Clodion, with chiselled gilt-bronze mounts and porphyry base, period of Louis Seize, made NF. 6,600 (£481); a fine *boiserie*, sculpted and painted with flower garlands, consisting of an alcove, two glazed doors, two doors, a pair of double doors, over-doors, and a chimney-piece in blue and white marble, formerly belonging to the Comte d'Artois, NF. 34,000 (£2,479); and another, carved, painted and gilded, with mirrors and a marble chimney piece, NF. 44,000 (£3,208).

A *suite* of six chairs, tapestry covered, with carved frames, period of Louis Quinze, and stamped Bovo, realised NF. 54,000 (£3,934); a small circular *guéridon* in gilt bronze with a top of lapis lazuli, attributed to Gouthière, NF. 61,000 (£4,449); a small oval table decorated with marquetry, and stamped R.V.L.C., end of the period of Louis Quinze, NF. 35,500 (£2,552); a pair of *encoignures* in lacquer with gilded bronze mounts, beginning of the Louis Quinze period, NF. 20,000 (£1,458); an unsigned large oval table in marquetry by David Roentgens, with chiselled gilt-bronze mounts, period of Louis Seize, NF. 35,000 (£2,552); a dog-kennel of carved and gilded wood and blue velvet, period of Louis Seize, inventory mark of Marie-Antoinette, stamped C. I. Sené, NF. 75,000 (£5,468); a small jewel-case in marquetry with gilt-bronze mounts, period of Louis Quinze, stamped M.V.R.B. NF. 52,000 (£3,791); a small circular *guéridon* with ebony veneering and gilt-bronze mounts, period of Louis Seize, stamped M. Carlin, NF. 152,000 (£11,070); a small circular table, by the same maker, inset with soft-paste Sèvres plaques painted with flowers, and with gilt-bronze mounts, early Louis Seize period, NF. 235,000 (£17,139); and a carpet from the Royal factory at Beauvais, Louis Seize period, NF. 126,000 (£9,187).

There were some important items in the porcelain section of the sale, a rare Chantilly plate decorated in polychrome with a hunting-scene making NF. 3,000 (£219); a soft-paste Sèvres *biscuit* bust of Louis Quinze, from the model by J.-B. Lemoyne, NF. 2,100 (£153); another of Mme du Barry, after Pajou, NF. 3,300 (£241); the *biscuit* group of *Pygmalion*, by Falconet, NF. 3,100 (£226); four Sèvres plates of 1775, decorated in polychrome and gold by Aloncle, NF. 10,000 (£729); a pair of Sèvres *cache-pots* in polychrome, from the Buffon service, decorated by Aloncle, 1780, NF. 21,000 (£1,531); an oval soup-tureen from Sèvres decorated with polychrome flowers on a fine green ground, old soft-paste, painting attributed to Aloncle, NF. 57,000 (£4,154); and a rare Vincennes cup and saucer decorated with children in landscapes, reserved on a yellow, gold-dotted ground, NF. 16,200 (£1,182).

An oval box in gold decorated with scenes after Molière, some signed W.B., and with rubies forming the lock, was bought for NF. 14,500 (£1,058); a gold rectangular box, decorated with pearls and tortoiseshell, by Jacques Toussaint-Lemire, 1743, NF. 37,500 (£2,734); and an oval miniature by J. Petitot, enamel on gold, a portrait of Lady Catherine Howard, signed and dated 1643, NF. 35,000 (£2,552).

In a sale of English furniture on 8th December Christie's sold a set of six Hepplewhite mahogany open armchairs in the French style for £787; a Regency pierced bronze and brass fender for £105; and a pair of similar andirons of the same period for £42. A pair of Chippendale open armchairs of fine quality, covered with floral grey damask, sold for £892; and a single armchair for £220. A mahogany kettle-stand of the same period, carved with medallions and strapwork, was bought for £273; a fine quality knee-hole writing desk for £892; and a later mahogany writing table, £525. A pair of Regency giltwood wall-lights, with eagles supporting the nozzles, 34″ high, sold for £378; and a mahogany circular breakfast table for £231. £399 was paid for a pair of large giltwood upright mirrors, the moulded borders and cresting carved with Oriental heads and flowering branches, 7′ 1″ high × 3′ 9″ wide; £210 for a Sheraton small mahogany writing-table; and the same amount for a small side-table of the period of George II.

Among the carpets, a good Kirman, 16′ 10″ × 11′ 4″, made £273; a silk carpet of Ispahan design, 9′ 6″ × 6′ 6″, £504; a Kashan carpet, 12′ × 9′, £262; and a Tabriz hunting carpet, 16′ 6″ × 12′ 3″, £546.

On the same day Sotheby sold a portrait of an unknown man by Frans Hals for £182,000, a price which provoked comment at the time. A speculative painting on panel, perhaps by Michelangelo, realised £13,000. The price suggests that the attribution did not receive wide acceptance. A Stubbs, *Baron Roebeck riding in Hyde Park*, sold for £20,000; £15,000 was paid for a flower piece by Jan (Velvet) Brueghel; and £5,000 for a basket of fruit from the same hand. A landscape by Jacob van Ruysdael sold for £8,500; another by Salomon van Ruysdael for £7,000; and a winter landscape by van der Neer for £7,600.

On 9th December a reclining female figure by Henry Moore was sold at Christie's for £5,775; and a *View of Trouville*, of 1885 by Boudin, for £5,040. *The Bathers*, of Othon Friesz, realised £1,470; the Chirico, *Horsemen on the Shore*, £1,260; and a bronze, 18½″ in height, *The Burgher of Calais*, by Rodin, £997.

The winter sale at the Dorotheum was held on 9th December. The *Kinder im Frühling*, signed and dated 1863, of Edmond Castan, on panel, formerly in the Viennese Imperial Collection, realised Sch. 25,000 (£338); *Die kleinen Sänger*, by the Munich painter, Franz von Defregger, signed, Sch. 32,000 (£434); *Caritas* by Willem Key (1520–1568), on panel, Sch. 25,000 (£338); *Am Ziehbrunnen*, on panel, signed by August von Pettenkofen, Sch. 50,000 (£677); Jacob van Ruysdael, *Blick auf Bad Spa*, a small edition of the picture in the Kaiser Friedrich Museum, Sch. 40,000 (£543); *Der heilige Karl Borromäus*, by Paul Troger, Sch. 120,000 (£1,624); *Das letzte Abend-mahl*, after the Tintoretto in San Trovaso, Venice, by El Greco, Sch. 100,000 (£1,354); a Chagall, *Automne*, ceramic, in nine colours, Sch. 180,000 (£2,438); and a pencil drawing by Egon Schiele, signed and dated 1915, of the captain of a prison camp at Mühling, Sch. 18,000 (£243). A baroque limewood carving of the Virgin standing on a globe, stamping on a snake, original colours including gold and silver, *c.* 1720, from

Upper Austria, Sch. 110,000 (£1,489). A Flemish tapestry of the late 17th century, woven with a still life and a flower border, realised Sch. 30,000 (£405).

A number of important clocks were included in the sale of 9th December at Sotheby. An attractive miniature walnut bracket-clock by Stephen Asselin, London, working about 1700, made £400; a basket-top kingwood bracket-clock by John Constantin, a little later, £300; a late 17th-century bracket-clock by Richard Colston, £230; and a John Knibb, with a 6¾″ dial, £850. A bracket-clock by his brother, Joseph Knibb, in the same sale made £950.

A marquetry long-case clock, by William Cattell, *Londini fecit*, of the late 17th century realised £420; a marquetry bracket-clock by George Etherington, Master of the Clockmaker's Company in 1709, £600; a fine walnut long-case clock, with a 10½″ dial, by John Knibb, £1,650; and a small double basket top bracket-clock by J. Windmills in original oak travelling-case, £620. A superb Roman-striking month bracket-clock by Joseph Knibb realised £1,750; a very fine Henry Jones bracket-clock, *c.* 1665, in a walnut case with panelled pediment cresting, £480; and an unusual 'perpetual motion' clock by James Cox, wound by barometric pressure, £600. A Louis Quinze ormolu mantel-clock, with a Turkish girl seated on rococo scrollwork, sold for £600; and a fine example by Charles Le Roy, the clock upheld by two Chinamen, £3,000.

Fine glass, too, was appreciating in value. A rare goblet engraved with the Arms of the Anti-Gallican Society, sold for £160; a goblet with a rare yellow and white basket-twist stem for £140; and a set of three engraved wine glasses, perhaps of Jacobite significance, for £145. A German ruby-glass beaker, carved with a bacchanalian scene in *hochschnitt*, of the end of the 17th century, realised £380; a fine Kunckel ruby-glass beaker and cover from Potsdam, by Gottfried Spiller, decorated in *hochschnitt* and *intaglio*, £850; a finely-engraved Silesian goblet and cover, with stags and boars in a rococo frame, £220; and a magnificent early Petersdorf portrait goblet and cover, 14″ high, by Friedrich Winter, with a portrait of Augustus the Strong of Saxony, belonging to the late 17th century, £900. An extremely rare enamelled Royal Armorial goblet, 9¼″ high, by Beilby of Newcastle-on-Tyne, sold for £1,820.

Rugs and carpets sold well, a small Bokhara carpet making £220; a Chinese carpet, 17′ 2″ × 11′, £260; a pair of finely-knotted Nahim rugs, 7′ × 4′ 8″, £270; an unusual Kirman carpet, 14′ 7″ × 10′ 2″, £340; and a brightly coloured Heraz carpet, 10′ 4″ × 9′ 4″, £540. An Aubusson carpet, 14′ 10″ × 11′ 6″, of floral pattern realised £520, and another, slightly larger, £620. A set of three Louis Quatorze tapestries, woven with scenes from the story of Abraham, realised £750; and a Louis Quinze Aubusson tapestry, woven with a *Fête Galante* in the style of Watteau, £360.

Two red japanned cabinets, each on well-carved stands, characteristic of late 17th-century work, made £720 apiece; and a Louis Quinze kingwood *guéridon*, signed by R. Lacroix, £2,100.

Paintings and drawings were sold at the Palais Galliéra on 9th December, a water-colour, *Pommes et Bouteille*, of Cézanne realising NF. 91,000 (£6,634), and another by the same artist, *Toits d'une ferme* NF. 25,000 (£1,823). A Dufy, *Vers New York*, signed, was sold for NF. 11,500 (£839); a Dunoyer de Segonzac, *En Provence*, signed, for NF. 48,000 (£3,499); the *Amazone et Dandy à Hyde Park* of Constantin Guys,

NF. 11,000 (£802); a Picasso, *Couple de dos*, a drawing in coloured pencil of 1899, NF. 17,500 (£1,276); the *Baigneuses* of Suzanne Valadon, in charcoal, slightly torn, NF. 4,100 (£300); a Vlaminck water-colour, *Le village aux toits rouges*, NF. 22,000 (£1,605); a ceramic *jardinière* by Gauguin, NF. 8,000 (£582); the *Bord de mer dans le Midi* of Braque, oil on canvas, signed and dated '07, NF. 60,000 (£4,374); the *Mariés de la Tour Eiffel* of Chagall, NF. 81,000 (£5,832); a Dufy of 1925, *Le Port de Marseille*, NF. 53,000 (£3,879); *Les canaux d'Anvers*, of Othon Friesz, NF. 25,600 (£1,823); *Le martyre de Saint Pierre* (after Titian), by Théodore Géricault, NF. 14,000 (£1,021); the *Nu au fauteuil* of Marcel Gromaire, signed and dated 1938, NF. 39,000 (£2,844); a Guillaumin, *Chemin sous les arbres*, NF. 15,000 (£1,094); another, *Potager devant le ferme*, NF. 12,000 (£875); another, *La Sablière*, NF. 11,500 (£839); *Le Bords de la Seine à Conflans en Automne* of Lebourg, signed, NF. 19,000 (£1,385); another, *Les Bords de la Seine à Herblay par temps de neige*, signed and dated 1895, NF. 23,000 (£1,677); a Maximilien Luce, *La Mare (Environs de Saint-Laurent-en-Caux)*, signed and dated '09, NF. 11,000 (£802); a Louis Marcoussis, *Oslo*, of 1928, NF. 13,000 (£948); a Picasso, *Nu endormi*, about 1903, NF. 95,000 (£7,558); another, *Melon et figures de Barbarie*, 1948, NF. 49,000 (£3,570); a Renoir, *Corbeille de Pêches*, signed, NF. 71,000 (£5,576); a *Nature morte aux fruits* by Nicolas de Staël, NF. 95,000 (£7,558); the *Paysage Parisien* of Utrillo, signed, NF. 20,000 (£1,458); a *Vase de fleurs*, of Louis Valtat, NF. 18,000 (£1,313); *Les acrobates* of Kees van Dongen (1904–5), NF. 35,000 (£2,553); Jacques Villon, *Portrait de Suzanne Duchamp*, signed and dated 1928, NF. 12,000 (£875); a Vlaminck *Le carrefour* of 1920, NF. 57,000 (£4,151); and the *Rue de Village sous la neige*, of the same artist, NF. 45,000 (£3,281).

Of the *tableaux anciens*, a *Vierge à l'adoration* of Gentile da Fabriano made NF. 25,100 (£1,830); a Parri di Spinello (Sienese School), *Vierge de Majesté*, on ogival panel, certified by Professor Adolfo Venturi, for NF. 15,300 (£1,116); a Galizia Fedé, *Coupe de Fruits*, NF. 12,000 (£875); *Les Pièces d'orfèvrerie*, by Wilhelm Kalf (Amsterdam 1622–1693), NF. 25,000 (£1,495); a portrait of Louis Quinze by Nattier, NF. 58,000 (£4,223); *La curée faite*, a *nature morte* of game-birds, a dead boar, and a dog, by Oudry, formerly known only as an engraving and recently rediscovered, NF. 55,000 (£4,005); *La Vierge et l'Enfant* by Tintoretto, authenticated by Professors Porcella and Venturi, NF. 37,000 (£2,697); and *Le concert dans le parc*, attributed to J. H. Tischbein the Elder, NF. 10,000 (£736).

An important sale of pictures held at the Palais Galliéra in Paris on 12th December included *Fruits et fleurs dans une corbeille* by Christien van Pol, signed, at NF. 14,800 (£1,080); *La Lecture de la lettre*, gouache, by J.-B. Mallet, NF. 17,000 (£1,240); a set of four paintings of naval manœuvres and battles, by Antoine Roux, water-colour and gouache, NF. 50,000 (£3,642); a *suite* of eight drawings, signed, illustrations for a book by Claude Anet, *Notes sur l'Amour*, by Bonnard, NF. 85,500 (£6,233); *Le Pesage*, a water-colour, by Dufy, NF 21,000 (£1,531); a pastel, *Femme au bord de la mer*, by Manet, NF. 130,000 (£9,480); a Picasso, *Coquelicots dans un vase, 31 mars 1943*, wash, signed, NF. 16,000 (£1,166); a pastel by Vuillard, *Femme dans un intérieur*, signed, NF. 20,100 (£1,465); *Plat rond présentant une Baigneuse a mi-corps*, a painting in enamel colours on a ceramic base, signed on the reverse and dated 1907, by Rouault,

NF. 15,000 (£1,094); *Yvette Guilbert en scène*, a typical painting in enamel colours on a ceramic base, monogram, by Toulouse-Lautrec, NF. 23,500 (£1,714); Courbet, *La Cascade*, oil on canvas, signed and dated, NF. 11,800 (£861); a Marie Laurencin, *Jeune fille aux colombes*, signed and dated 1921, NF. 17,500 (£1,276); the *Bords de la Seine à Suresnes*, of Lebourg, signed, NF. 13,000 (£948); the *Dernier froid* of Alfred Manessier, signed and dated 1957, NF. 12,500 (£911); a Marquet, *Port d'Alger*, signed, NF, 25,000 (£1,822); *Jeune fille en robe blanche, Juin 1941* of Matisse, NF. 100,000 (£7,292); a *Nature morte* by the same artist, NF. 71,000 (£5,176); the *Nymphéas* of Monet, signed, NF. 145,000 (£10,573); *Composition en noir, rouge et blanc* by Miro, NF. 55,000 (£4,007); *La Blonde* by Jules Pascin, signed, painted on cardboard with oil-paint diluted with spirit, NF. 21,000 (£1,531); the *Nocturne chrétien*, signed, of Rouault, NF. 48,000 (£3,499); three oil-paintings by Utrillo, *Vue de Montmagny*, signed, NF. 24,500 (£1,779), *Paris, rue de Clovis*, NF. 49,000 (£3,572), and *Le Lapin agile*, signed, NF. 70,500 (£5,140); *Nu debout* by Suzanne Valadon, NF. 24,000 (£1,750); the *Fleurs dans un vase* by Vlaminck, NF. 40,000 (£2,916); *Paysage aux Meules* by the same artist, NF. 45,500 (£3,317); *Intérieur* by Vuillard, NF. 32,000 (£2,326); a pen drawing, *Femme se maquillant*, by Picasso, NF. 23,000 (£1,677); a water-colour, *La Baie de Saint-Tropez*, by Dunoyer de Segonzac, NF. 26,000 (£1,895); *La Mer*, oil on canvas, by Kees van Dongen, signed, NF. 70,700 (£5,159); the *Paysan travaillant* by van Gogh, NF. 100,000 (£7,292); *Tournesol géant sur fond vert*, signed, by Bernard Lorjon, NF. 20,500 (£1,495); *Le Pont Neuf vu du quai des Grands Augustins* of Marquet, signed, NF. 46,500 (£3,389).

Furniture in the same sale included a small circular marquetry table with ormolu mounts of the Louis Quinze period, with the stamp of Topino, which sold for NF. 28,000 (£2,041); a small marquetry bureau of the same period, with ormolu mounts, NF. 27,500 (£2,005); a *secretaire* in mahogany with ormolu mounts, stamped J. Dautriche, NF. 27,500 (£2,005); a Louis Seize marquetry commode with ormolu mounts, stamped P. Denizot, NF. 10,600 (£773); a Régence writing-table with a leather top, NF. 20,700 (£1,509); a commode in wood and brown lacquer of the Louis Seize period, with ormolu mounts, stamped P. F. Guignard, NF. 17,100 (£1,248). A series of twelve marble pillars, arranged in pairs on an ormolu base, surmounted by sculptured human and animal figures, formerly part of the upper gallery in the cloister of the Cathedral of d'Elne, 14th century, with some restorations, realised NF. 28,000 (£2,041).

On the same day, at Sotheby in London, a bronze Egyptian cat of the Saite period, 13″ high, was bought for £1,200; an Attic red-figure krater for £1,000; another, showing Menelaus and Helen, for £850; and a 3rd-century Gandhara grey schist Buddha, 27″ high, for £900.

Prints of one kind or another have been returning to favour in recent years, and Sotheby's sale of 12th December was an excellent guide to current market values. The result is, therefore, given at some length.

For the most part the highest prices were given for those artists whose paintings are in the greatest demand in the sale-room. *Le Bain*, a signed lithograph by Bonnard, sold for £45, and the *Les Cigales et les Fourmis*, one of 50 proofs of Gauguin, for £65.

Another Gauguin, *Portrait de Stephane Mallarmé*, an etching of 1891, made £120; the *Projet d'Assiette*, one of about 50 proofs with touches of water colour, £120; and the *Titres du Sourire*, a woodcut numbered 23, signed with monogram, £45.

The Matisse, *Odalisque Assise à la Jupe de Dentelle*, a signed lithograph, sold for £110, and another signed lithograph, *Nu Jambe Repliée*, for £60. *Black Eyes*, a lithograph of 1914, realised £95; another, *Modèle au Fourrure Blanc*, signed, £122; a linoleum cut, *Nude with a Necklace*, signed, £65; and *Les Deux Odalisques*, by J. Villon after Matisse, signed Matisse, for £34. Of several aquatints, by Georges Rouault, *En bouche sur fut fraiche gout de fiel* realised £32, and a lithograph, *Les Clowns*, £42. An etching by Renoir, *Le Chapeau Epinglé*, sold for £30; and a lithograph, signed, by Camille Pissarro, *Baigneuses Luttant*, £95. The *Rue Saint-Lazare, Paris*, by the same artist, went for £50.

As might have been expected, the work of Toulouse-Lautrec was much in demand. A lithograph, *Yahne dans sa Loge*, made £96; *Mlle Pois Vert*, £160; *Au Hanneton*, £270; *Mlle Marcelle Lender, en Buste*, £95; and *Femme en Corset*, £60. Three signed woodcuts by Felix Vallotton sold for £24, £24, and £30 respectively, and a portrait of Maurice Utrillo, a signed lithograph dated 1928, by Suzanne Valodon, sold for £14. *The Haystacks*, a signed lithograph by Vlaminck, realised £28, whilst two lithographs by Edouard Vuillard, *L'Atre* and *Projet de Couverture pour un Album d'Estampes*, made £90 and £32. A lithograph, signed, by Georges Braque, *Helios II*, sold for £60; and the *Oiseau sur fond carmin*, a signed aquatint, £100. A signed lithograph, *Le Jour*, by Joan Miró, realised £24; a signed aquatint, *Personage*, £48; and a poster, *Galerie Maegt Exhibition*, a signed lithograph, £38.

The work of Picasso was much in demand, *Le Repas Frugal*, a signed etching of 1904, selling for £260. Another specimen sold at the Galerie Charpentier in Paris on 17th June realised 5,500 francs (£380). *Salomé*, a drypoint of 1905, sold for £160; *Le Chef d'Œuvre Inconnu*, twelve etchings of 1927, signed, £1,400; a signed lithograph, *Nature Morte au Livre*, £70; and *Les Deux Saltimbanques*, after Picasso by J. Villon, an aquatint, for £52.

The *St Germain des Prés*, a signed lithograph of 1954 by Chagall, was sold for £115; *Le Christ à l'horloge*, another of 1957, for £48; and *Bouquet Vert*, for £60.

Of the work of Kokoschka, *Portrait of Paul Westheim*, a lithograph signed, realised £32, and *Bildnis (auf die Hand gestützter Kopf)* of 1955, £28. The *Brustbild einer Arbeiterfrau mit blauem Tuch* of 1903, by Käthe Kollwitz, was sold for £28, and *Die Pflüger*, an etching and aquatint of 1906, signed, by the same artist, for £20. The *Heyerdahl Sisters*, a signed lithograph, by Edvard Munch, made £85. The etchings of Anders Zorn were cheap enough. *Mona*, signed and dated 1911, made £36, but most of the others could be bought for a few pounds. Of the work of Meryon, an etching of 1850, first state signed in pencil, *Le Petit Pont, Paris*, sold for £230, and *La Rue des Toiles à Bourges*, third state of 1853, at £60.

English prints were not in great demand, although *A Spanish Good Friday, Ronda*, a drypoint by Muirhead Bone, realised £210. Another drypoint by the same artist, signed, of Rabindranath Tagore was sold for £26. *An Early Riser* by Seymour Haden was bought for £80, and two etchings, both signed, by Augustus John, *The Serving Maid* and

The Jewess, brought £12 and £14 respectively. The *Barcarolle*, a signed etching by James McBey, sold for £46, and, of the Whistlers in the sale, *Black Lion Wharf* brought £28; *Becquet*, a portrait, £23; *Rotherhithe*, £38; *Speke Hall* of 1870, £52; the *Little Nude Model*, a lithograph, £34; and *Little Dordrecht*, the original etched plate sold with an autograph letter dated 1887, and a Spy cartoon signed with both name and butterfly, for £32. The Brockhurst, *Adolescence*, an etching of 1932, signed, sold for £28.

At an important sale of Chinese works of art at Sotheby on 13th December a pair of yellow glazed bowls with the mark of Yung Chêng (1723–1735), the exterior incised and glazed in green with boys at play, realised £340; an Imperial etched bowl with two dragons painted in shades of green, yellow, and aubergine, of the K'ang Hsi period (1662–1722), £210; a T'ang (618–906) equestrienne pottery figure, $15\frac{1}{2}''$ high, with traces of pigment, £200; a Chün bowl of the Sung dynasty (960–1279), £155; and a lobed melon-shaped spouted ewer, 3″ high, with a *kinuta* glaze, of the Sung dynasty for £165. A ewer similar in shape and glaze, but larger in size, was sold earlier in the year for £540. A large early 15th-century blue-and-white dish, 20″ diameter, decorated with lotus and other foliage, realised £220; whilst another, slightly smaller, of the same period, decorated with peonies, and of magnificent quality, brought £800. A fine pair of bowls decorated in underglaze copper red with three fruits, Yung Chêng period, sold for £290; a large *Compagnie des Indes* tureen, cover, and stand with European flowers, £360; an unusual pair of seated hounds of the Ch'ien Lung period (1736–1795), 22″ high, £900; and a large dinner service painted in *famille rose* colours, partly Ch'ien Lung porcelain and partly replacements from the Worcester factory of Chamberlain, in all 124 pieces, £660.

A superbly carved Ch'ien Lung jade vase and cover of pale green colour, with loose ring handles, one joined by a jade link chain, sold for £640; and an important *ting* and cover, of rectangular section, of the same period, $13\frac{1}{2}''$ in height, magnificently carved in pale green translucent jade, £1,650.

An important Ming bronze figure of a Boddhisattva, 28 inches high, of the 16th century, and formerly in a Pekin Temple, sold for £114.

Modern English drawings, painting, and sculpture formed the subject of Sotheby's sale on 14th December, and a number of Max Beerbohm drawings sold for a total of £2,580.

A still life by Matthew Smith made £550; a sleeping model, £750; a landscape, £1,100; and *Apples on a wicker chair*, painted in 1915, £900. Sickert's portrait of Mrs Barrett, painted in 1908, made £1,500; a Jamaican landscape by Augustus John, £400; and *Thorn Apple Flowers* by Graham Sutherland, £400.

Julia amidst the Sands by Russell Flint fetched £440; *One Summer Day*, £420; and *Sands at Bamburgh, Northumberland*, £240.

A bronze by Henry Moore of a mother and child, one of nine, 1956, sold for £1,500; another, *Thin Reclining Figure* (one of nine, 1953), for £1,200; a *Leaf Figure*, one of nine, 1952, £850; and a reclining figure, one of seven, 1945, £1,000. A drawing, studies for the Northampton *Madonna and Child*, sold for £900, and a standing nude, £240. An Epstein bronze, *Euphemia Lamb*, sold for £300, and the head of the child, *Leda*, for £550.

On the same day Christie's sold four silver sauceboats by John Emes, of 1799, for £300. A George II pear-shaped coffee-pot by Christian Hillard (29 oz.) realised £500, a dinner-service by Henry Greenway (162 oz.), £620; a George II cream-jug by John Schuppe, 1754, £260; a teapot by Gabriel Sleath, 1730, £245; and a Louis Quinze silver-gilt *écuelle* and cover, Strasbourg, 1750, £460.

At Christie's on 15th December a panel of Beauvais tapestry, inscribed *Behagle*, depicting huntsmen and staghounds in a landscape, sold for £1,522; a gilt-bronze clock of Louis Quinze period, with added porcelain flowers, for £2,310; and a set of four South German terracotta nymphs symbolising the Seasons for £756.

On 16th December at Sotheby the remarkable price of £210 was paid for a pair of boys in Court dress on cut-out board, sometimes known as 'comforters'. A pair of rococo wall-mirrors sold for £420; an Adam side-board in mahogany for £520; and a Chinese carpet of good quality for £500. A violin by J. B. Guadignini of Turin, dated 1785, realised £1,150.

An interesting sale of pottery and porcelain at Sotheby on 20th December included some rare items. £150 was paid for a pair of small tureens in the form of partridges from Proskau; and a late Meissen tureen, cover and stand painted with birds, of the Marcolini period, made £100. A pair of Paris vases of campagna shape painted with garden flowers made £200; a Meissen figure of a dancing Harlequin, £460; a Paris part-dessert service of 85 pieces, by Darte Frères, £280; a Flight, Barr & Barr Worcester dessert service of 33 pieces (the 'Royal Lily' pattern), £155; and a good dinner service of the same origin, with floral medallions and borders on a copper red ground, 76 pieces, £420.

A Chelsea tureen and cover in the form of a melon, red anchor mark, made £580; a pair of Flight, Barr & Barr Worcester vases painted with scenes from Shakespeare, perhaps by Thomas Baxter, £125; and a pair of Bloor Derby vases of campagna shape, the covers modelled as bouquets of flowers, the sides similarly decorated, with rich blue grounds, £310.

English pottery sold well, an Astbury-Whieldon figure of an actor realising £100; a rare Whieldon Dovecot, £210; a Ralph Wood Sweep, after Cyfflé, £60; a pair of good Liverpool delft flower-holders of brick shape, painted in colours, £115; an important Lambeth delft octagonal pill-slab, with the Arms of the Apothecaries' Company, painted in colours, £580; a salt-glaze Jacobite tea-pot and cover of pecten shell form, £95; and a rare Lambeth delft dish, after Palissy, decorated with the subject of *La Fecondité* in relief, and coloured, with the date 1661, £480.

Sotheby held their final sale of 1960 on 22nd December when Sir James Mann, buying for the Tower of London Armouries, bought a rare German or Flemish wheel-lock petronel of 1581 for £2,100—the highest price ever recorded for a single pistol. A London Colt of 1849, a five-shot percussion-cap type, made £190; and a Navy model of 1851, £290. A New York Colt of 1851, engraved with a paddle boat and sailing ships, sold for £440. In the same sale a Limoges *champlevé* enamel cross was sold for £720, and an early 16th-century Flemish woodcarving for £330. A large carved oak relief of about 1500 of the Holy Family, perhaps South German, was bought for £580.

Many items of interest and importance were sold throughout the year in the London rooms of Phillip, Sons & Neale, of which the following is a selection. A pair of *encoignures* of Louis Quinze design, £520; a Boulle style octagonal tray-top table, £480; a commode in the style of Boulle, £250; a pair of Hepplewhite mahogany cross-banded side-tables, £600; an early Meissen bowl decorated with *chinoiseries*, £600; a Queen Anne walnut bureau-bookcase, with mirror-glass panelled doors, £1,900; a kingwood *bombé* commode in the Régence style, £580; a set of six Hepplewhite open armchairs upholstered in crimson damask, £1,220; a Savonnerie carpet woven with scrolls and flowers, £1,100; *Flowers in a basket*, School of Bosschaert, oil on panel, £2,100; a Swansea porcelain dessert service painted with flowers, 20 pieces, £620; an Irish plain, shaped chocolate pot by Robert Calderwood, £660; a pair of Sheraton side-tables, veneered with mahogany and rosewood, £820; an unusual Pembroke table of mahogany, £400; a large Samarkand rug, 13' 9" × 6' 11", £350; a crystal gold and enamel box with diamond borders by Fabergé, £600; a rare Sheraton reniform table veneered with amboyna, and a marquetry motif of flowers, £700; a Louis Quinze commode of kingwood and parquetry, with *rouge* marble top, £1,500; a 19th-century 2-tier side-table in the French taste in mahogany, with ormolu mounts and white marble top, £500; a Brueghel, *Festival in the square of a town on a river*, £780; *Woman and Child*, by Joan Miró, £370; and a Chippendale mahogany commode with carved decoration, £760.

CURRENCY CONVERSION

For the purpose of converting foreign currency into sterling, the following rates have been used:

American dollar	2·80 to the £.
Austrian schilling	74·00 to the £.
French new franc	13·75 to the £.

This, of course, takes no account of minor fluctuations, but is accurate enough for practical purposes. Prices quoted are to the nearest £.

In comparing 1960 prices with those realised before 1939, the following estimate of the present-day value of the £ is realistic:

1918–1939	5s 8½d.
1900–1914	4s.
before 1900	2s. 6d.

Where the original price was in guineas, it has been quoted to the nearest £, for the sake of clarity. Similarly, the weight of silver has been quoted to the nearest ounce.

price trends

in the principal categories

If current market prices are examined and compared with those of the past, making due allowance for the devaluation of currency, two fairly distinct trends begin to emerge. Collecting can, in fact, be described as ambivalent. On the one hand there is a demand for an art which is primarily emotional in its appeal, satisfied by the paintings of the Impressionists, the post-Impressionists, and their successors, as well as by primitive art such as that of Africa; on the other, there is a growing demand for the luxury product—the trappings of prestige—which can be seen particularly in the prices paid for 18th-century French furniture and decoration.

Although the market in old Master paintings was steady, price levels continued lower than in the not very remote past, except in a few isolated instances some of which were hardly explicable on rational grounds. The work of the English Victorians, to much of which the line:

'He fell upon his hands in warm wet slop'

by the contemporary Poet-Laureate, Alfred Austin, is curiously appropriate, continued to sell at a mere fraction of the prices given in the 19th century, although, at the end of the year, we were threatened with a Landseer Exhibition at the Royal Academy. The market for Impressionist and later painting, however, seemed insatiable. Although it is true that there were some instances in which higher prices were given than those paid for contemporary art in the 19th century, it is doubtful whether any modern artist has yet achieved the income of Millais, who is reputed to have made £40,000 in a single year from the sale of paintings and reproduction rights. Unlike '*Bubbles*', Picasso has yet to make his appearance on the hoardings.

In the last hundred and fifty years the nature of art has changed radically. Formerly, paintings were commissioned for a specific setting, which imposed a salutary discipline on the painter. Like the cabinet-maker, the silversmith, and the porcelain manufacturer, the painter of pictures was also a craftsman who took orders from his client. The latter specified his requirements—ecclesiastical or secular—and controlled almost everything except the style in which the work was executed. He ordered a subject to fit his drawing-room, to be placed in a particular position, and not a state of mind. Art has now changed in direction and intention, and it is still too early to say whether anything of permanent value is likely to emerge. Certainly, on the lunatic fringe, high prices are given for things in which paint is applied to canvas in a manner entirely fortuitous, which is the complete negation of craftsmanship.

The student of art today is faced with unprecedented difficulties. For good or ill, most of the things which surround him are made by unskilled or semi-skilled artisans on a production line. They are made to appeal to the lowest common denominator in the community, to a design which market-research shows will be bought most freely. In almost every department of life quality is being sacrificed to quantity and planned obsolescence. It is, therefore, only with an effort of will that he can enter and share the world of the earlier craftsmen, to whom patient skill, and the quality of design and materials, were all-important, and who tried to make things of permanent value.

Turning to the prices quoted, it is hazardous to draw conclusions from them, but some are reasonably safe. Few changes are to be anticipated in the immediate future in the market for Impressionists and post-Impressionists. They are now old enough to be certain that their popularity is not ephemeral. Neither should it be, for no one can deny their stature as great artists. In more recent work, however, many reputations remain to be confirmed, although that of Picasso and a few others is well enough established. Prices for his work are high, but they are not historically high when adjustments have been made for the depreciation in currency values. As much was paid for contemporary art in the 19th century when the work of the period was being bought by rich industrialists. The test will come not in the next few decades, but in a century or two, when modern art as a whole can be seen in perspective. Whether these will become the old Masters of tomorrow, however, is not a question which need trouble us today. Work of this character is in keeping with modern styles in interior decoration, and whilst these remain what they are, prices are not likely to move in any but an upward direction for much of it.

Current values for 18th-century French furniture are not new. Comparable prices were being paid in the middle of the 19th century when some of it was less than seventy years old. The large increases to be noticed in the price of good 19th-century reproductions suggests very strongly that antique value takes second place to its undoubted value as interior decoration. Skilful craftsmanship, now almost non-existent, and exotic and expensive materials, will always command their price, and the best reproductions are not noticeably poorer in these qualities than the originals they copy. It became noticeable during the year that such accessories as ormolu wall-lights, mounted porcelain candelabra, clocks, *chenets*, and similar things were following the prices of French furniture upwards.

Prices for English furniture of high quality were good, but, relatively, they were on a lower level. This was not due to quality because, at its best, it is extremely good. Like old Master painting, however, it is also at its best in surroundings which are, at present, slightly unfashionable. Least valued was 17th-century oak furniture. Apparently this was felt hardly worth putting into the sale-room, since it appeared but rarely. Oak-beamed country houses and cottages are disappearing. Even 'Stockbroker's Tudor' is giving place to a bastard style referred to approvingly by one Councillor charged with preserving rural amenities as 'New Traditional'. Old oak furniture is absurd in such settings, and, except for really exceptional specimens, it seems unlikely to be in much demand for some time to come. Probably the highest prices, in ratio to quality and design, were given for things made towards the end of the 18th century, when English makers were inspired by those of France. This, however, is a passing phase and throughout the year a slow but steady appreciation in price for earlier 18th-century work was noticeable. Oriental rugs remained undervalued, due, once again, to the style of interior decoration popular. They are at their best with English furniture, old oil paintings, and old delft pottery. Nevertheless, the quality of the older rugs will certainly not be repeated, and they remain the most attractive form of floor-covering. Aubusson carpets made excellent prices, despite the fact that the tapestry-weave makes them more vulnerable to wear and damage than pile carpets. They are, however, almost essential to any scheme of decoration using fine French furniture.

Renaissance and 17th-century furniture and decoration continued to be low in price, although the few good bronzes which came onto the market sold well. Italian *maiolica* in many instances could be bought more cheaply than its importance warranted. Here again, prices are suffering from the current style in interior decoration. Most tapestries, too, were inexpensive. Few people now have walls capable of taking any but the smallest effectively.

Much 16th- and 17th-century silver seemed undervalued, except for such things as early spoons. Eighteenth-century work, however, appreciated considerably during the year, and the tendency was particularly noticeable with rococo silver. Such masters of the style as Paul de Lamerie were in especial demand, but the earlier plain silver of Queen Anne also found eager buyers. Prices for de Lamerie silver can be not unfairly connected with the demand for Louis Quinze furniture. Appreciation in later silver followed a curve less steep, although Hester Bateman continued in demand for no very good reason.

A feature of the market was the high prices paid for Scandinavian silver whenever it appeared. This, in design and quality, did not noticeably excel a good deal of comparable English silver which sold at lower prices. Prices for French silver were extremely good, two important examples being the £207,000 obtained at Sotheby for the Berkeley Castle service by Jacques Roettiers and the £10,573 for a ewer and stand by Nicolas de Launay at the Palais Galliéra, but good French silver is much rarer than English. Both Louis Quatorze and Louis Quinze consigned large quantities to the Mint to be used as coinage, and the Revolution accounted for a great deal more.

The publication of a book dealing with the rococo period during the year (*The Age of Rococo*, Schönberger and Söhner, London) seemed not inappropriate. The finest work in this style in porcelain was done by Franz Anton Bustelli of Nymphenburg, and his figures sold exceptionally well whenever they appeared. This is nothing new, and he has been popular for several years past. In porcelain generally, however, there was a movement away from the less spectacular early wares towards those which could fairly be described as colourful decoration. At the moment the focus appears to have shifted slightly, and some early things of importance could be bought at prices very little above those of four or five years ago; in some cases, even for less. This applied particularly to English porcelain, and seems to be a temporary phase caused by the disappearance of a few collectors of early wares from the market. This is merely temporary, however, and a new generation will appear in due time.

In the field of 18th-century English porcelain that of Worcester is the most colourful, and prices here have risen. In keeping with the demand for small and portable things are the high prices realised for Chelsea scent-bottles, and for important snuff-boxes, and so forth from this and the great Continental factories. This is a slightly different market, and equally high prices were realised throughout the year for such things as the work of the Czar's Court jeweller, Fabergé, and for gold-boxes and miniatures.

Somewhat inexplicably, French porcelain continued to be undervalued for the most part, despite a few instances of good prices being obtained. Sèvres, in particular, was inexpensive for all but the most important things, although there were a number of instances in London and Paris of high prices being paid for early cups and saucers with more than usually fine decoration.

Good German porcelain appreciated considerably, not only for the work of Meissen and du Paquier, Vienna, but for the minor factories, including those of Thuringia. Here again, however, the highest prices were paid for colourful decoration, and early work was not so much in demand. The *chinoiseries* of Meissen were especially sought after, but the work of this factory after about 1755 continued to be low in price. Good figures by Kändler sold well, but are still very much under prices realised for those of Bustelli, whilst the surprise of the season was the £1,000 apiece paid for fifteen figures from the Italian Comedy by Simon Feilner, a modeller known in England to only a few until a year or two ago.

Whilst the market in Chinese porcelain and works of art generally did not show the large increases to be seen in some other fields, a steady and general appreciation was noticeable. Anything of importance coming onto the market sold easily and well. The focus of interest seems to change little, but the demand in porcelain has probably shifted slightly away from the Sung dynasty towards the Yüan and early Ming periods. In Paris a sale of porcelain typically in the French taste underlined the difference between that of France and England. English collectors prefer wares in the Chinese 'classic' tradition, whilst those of France are more interested in the brilliantly-coloured spectacular wares of the later Ming and Ch'ing periods. Jades sold extremely well throughout the year, and what would have been regarded as very high prices a few years ago were almost commonplace. Increasing interest in Japanese art, too, has been evident.

Throughout the year there has been a steady appreciation in prices, and there have been very few fields in which this has not taken place. In European antiques the particular focus seems to be on things made in the first seventy years or so of the 18th century, and neo-classicism still does not appeal to modern taste to the same extent. English Regency, however, was much in demand in London, New York, and Paris. The first sales of the New Year suggested that the trends of 1960 would be continued in 1961, although, perhaps, some slackening in the rate at which prices have been rising will be noticeable. At present there are no signs of a movement likely to change general demand seriously in any particular direction.

illustrated catalogue

of important sale-room items

J. M. W. Turner (1775–1851)
Llanthony Abbey, Monmouth c. 1834
SOTHEBY & CO
November 30th 1960   £5,000

Bernardo Strozzi (1581–1644)
Architecture
PARKE-BERNET GALLERIES
October 19th 1960 $14,000 (£5,000)

Jan van Goyen (1596–1656)
A River Scene, on panel, signed and
dated 1647
CHRISTIE, MANSON & WOODS, LTD
April 1st 1960 £9,450

Francesco di Gentile da Fabriano
(1370–1427)
Madonna and Child
CHRISTIE, MANSON & WOODS, LTD
July 15th 1960 £945

James Pollard
*North Country Mail at the Peacock,
Islington*
SOTHEBY & CO
November 30th 1960 £19,000

Edgar Degas (1834–1917)
Trois Jockeys Pastel
PARKE-BERNET GALLERIES
October 26th 1960 $65,000 (£23,205)

Francesco Guardi (1712–1793)
Isola S. Giorgio Maggiore, Venice
PARKE-BERNET GALLERIES
November 12th 1960 $10,550 (£3,748)

Abraham Bosschaert (17th century
Dutch School)
Flowers in a basket, on panel
PHILLIPS, SON & NEALE
May 24th 1960 £2,100

Jean Auguste Dominique Ingres
(1780–1867)
Nude Drawing
PARKE-BERNET GALLERIES
October 26th 1960 $1,900 (£679)

Carel Fabritius (1622–1654)
Portrait of Rembrandt
CHRISTIE, MANSON & WOODS, LTD
April 1st 1960 £14,700

Salomon van Ruysdael (1600–1670)
The Ferry Boat
CHRISTIE, MANSON & WOODS, LTD
April 1st 1960 £15,750

The Aragonese Master Spanish c. 1450
The Legend of S. Michael and Galgano;
a six-panelled altar-piece
PARKE-BERNET GALLERIES
November 12th 1960 $10,000 (£3,571)

Sir Anthony van Dyck (1599–1641)
Portrait of a Woman
CHRISTIE, MANSON & WOODS, LTD
July 1st 1960 £6,300

Frans Snyders (1579–1657)
Still-life with pheasant
DOROTHEUM
September 13th 1960 Sch. 60,000
(£804)

Meindert Hobbema (1638–1700)
A Wooded River Scene, on panel
CHRISTIE, MANSON & WOODS, LTD
April 1st 1960 £14,700

Jacob Robusti (Tintoretto) (1518–1594)
Portrait of a Prelate
PARKE-BERNET GALLERIES
October 19th 1960 $14,000 (£5,000)

Dosso Dossi (1479–1542)
Allegorical figure with Cupid
PARKE-BERNET GALLERIES
October 19th 1960 $17,000 (£6,071)

Jacob Willemsz de Wet (1610–1672)
Christus ruft die kinder zu sich Signed,
on panel
DOROTHEUM
June 21st 1960 Sch. 40,000 (£557)

J. M. W. Turner R.A. (1775–1851)
Port Ruysdael
PARKE-BERNET GALLERIES
October 19th 1960 $31,000 (£11,068)

Alessandro Magnasco (1677–1749)
A Wooded Landscape
CHRISTIE, MANSON & WOODS, LTD
April 1st 1960 £10,500

Georges Rouault (1871–1958)
Potentate: Pierrot
PARKE-BERNET GALLERIES
October 26th 1960 $35,000 (£12,495)

Georges Braque (c. 1882)
La Barque Pavoisée Signed 1939
SOTHEBY & CO
July 6th 1960 £9,500

Honoré Daumier (1808–1879)
Le Wagon de Troisième Classe On
panel
SOTHEBY & CO
May 4th 1960 £2,250

Pierre Bonnard (1867–1947)
La Ferme à Vernon
CHRISTIE, MANSON & WOODS, LTD
May 20th 1960 £14,175

Pierre Bonnard (1867–1947)
Femme Nue
SOTHEBY & CO
July 6th 1960 £18,000

Amadeo Modigliani (1884–1920)
Boy with red hair 1919
SOTHEBY & CO
November 23rd 1960   £21,000

Pierre Bonnard (1867–1947)
Le Jardin du Peintre Signed c. 1925
SOTHEBY & CO
July 6th 1961 £9,000

P. Wilson Steer (1860–1942)
The Negro Page
CHRISTIE, MANSON & WOODS, LTD
May 20th 1960 £1,365

Maurice Vlaminck (1876–1958)
Französische Kleinstadt (Petite ville de France) c. 1908
DOROTHEUM
June 21st 1960 Sch. 250,000 (£3,377)

Eugene Boudin (1824–1898)
On the beach, Berck Signed and dated
CHRISTIE, MANSON & WOODS, LTD
May 20th 1960 £4,200

Paul Signac (1863–1935)
The Piazzetta, Venice Water-colour
PARKE-BERNET GALLERIES
October 26th 1960 $2,200 (£786)

Maurice Vlaminck (1879–1958)
Paysage (Rue de Village)
PARKE-BERNET GALLERIES
26th October 1960 $10,000 (£3,570)

Maurice Utrillo (1883–1955)
Eglise St. Pierre signed and dated 15th
October 1910
CHRISTIE, MANSON & WOODS, LTD
20th May 1960 £7,350

Maurice Vlaminck (1876–1958)
Hotel du Laboureur, Rueil-la-Gadelière
PARKE-BERNET GALLERIES
October 26th 1960 $22,000 (£7,854)

Camille Pissarro (1851–1903)
Avant Port de Dieppe Signed and dated
1902
PARKE-BERNET GALLERIES
October 26th 1960 $35,000 (£12,495)

Henri Matisse (1869–1954)
Black Eyes Lithograph 1914
SOTHEBY & CO
December 12th 1960 £95

Henri Matisse (1869–1954)
Odalisque assise à la jupe de dentelle
Lithograph Signed c. 1925
SOTHEBY & CO
December 12th 1960 £110

Henri Matisse (1869–1954)
Haitian Woman Drawing Signed and
dated, March 1945
PARKE-BERNET GALLERIES
October 26th 1960 $2,250 (£803)

Pierre Auguste Renoir (1841–1919)
Baigneuse debout dans l'eau Signed and
dated, 1888
SOTHEBY & CO
23rd November 1960 £38,000

Amadeo Modigliani (1884–1920)
Boy in a Green Suit
PARKE-BERNET GALLERIES
October 26th 1960 $57,500 (£20,627)

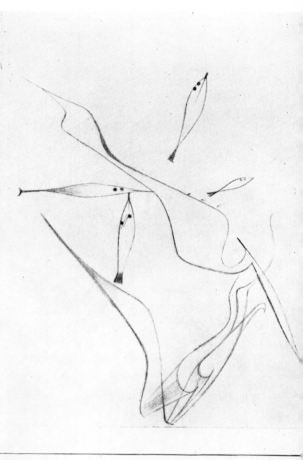

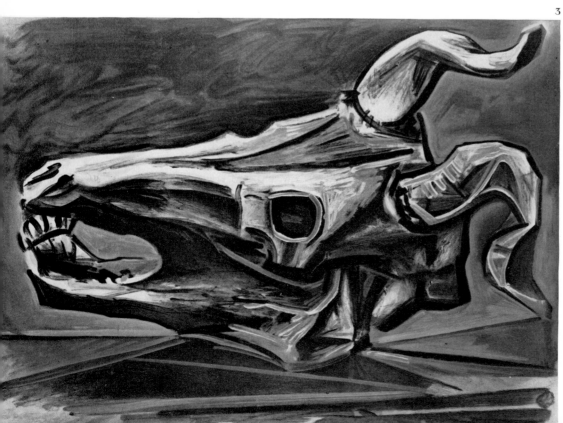

1   2

3

4   *Bon à tirer* Picasso

5

1. Henri Matisse (1869–1954)
Modèle au Fourrure Blanc Lithograph
c. 1929–30
SOTHEBY & CO
December 12th 1960 £122

2. Paul Klee (1879–1940)
Fischzauber Pencil drawing, study for
an oil Signed and dated 1924
DOROTHEUM
September 13th 1960 Sch. 22,000
(£279)

3. Pablo Picasso (b. 1881)
Crâne sur la table Aquatint-engraving
Signed
DOROTHEUM
December 6th 1960 Sch. 8,000 (£108)

4. Pablo Picasso (b. 1881)
Le Chef d'Œuvre Inconnu One of
twelve trial proofs, all signed and
inscribed '*Bon à tirer*' Etching 1927
SOTHEBY & CO
December 12th 1960 £1,400

5. Pablo Picasso (b. 1881)
Le Repas Frugal Etching 1904
SOTHEBY & CO
December 12th 1960 £260

Henri de Toulouse-Lautrec (1864–1901)
Au Hanneton ou à la Brasserie
Lithograph 1898
SOTHEBY & CO
December 12th 1960 £270

Marc Chagall (b. 1887)
St. Germain des Prés Lithograph 1954
Signed *Epreuve d'artiste*
SOTHEBY & CO
December 12th 1960 £115

Georges Braque (b. 1882)
Oiseau sur fond carmin aquatint 1958
SOTHEBY & CO
December 12th 1960 £100 ➡

Paul Gauguin (1848–1903)
Projet d'Assiette Zincograph 1889
SOTHEBY & CO
December 12th 1960 £120

Paul Gauguin (1848–1903)
Portrait of Stephane Mallarmé Etching
1891 SOTHEBY & CO
December 12th 1960 £120

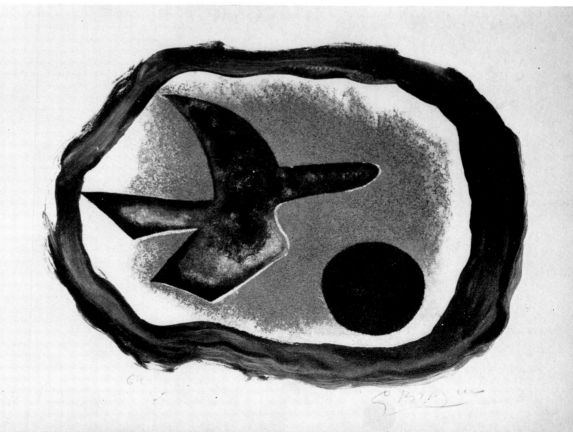

Gothic parcel-gilt alabaster altar-piece,
formerly in the Cloister of Poblet,
near Barcelona
PARKE-BERNET GALLERIES
November 12th 1960 $16,000 (£5,713)

The celebrated bronze thurible of Godric
—the Pershore Censer. English.
10th-11th century
SOTHEBY & CO
June 17th 1960   £2,600

South German limewood carving of
Mary, Elizabeth, and Zacharias c. 1515
DOROTHEUM
December 5th 1960 Sch. 30,000 (£402)

A fine Gothic carved wood portrait bust
with traces of polychrome colouring.
French. 15th century
PARKE-BERNET GALLERIES
November 12th 1960 $3,000 (£1,071)

Two *putti* in the baroque style as torch
holders
DOROTHEUM
March 18th 1960 Sch. 16,000 (£216)

Andrea della Robbia, Florence. A very important glazed terracotta lunette of the Archangel Michael. Executed in 1475 for the Church of S. Michele Arcangelo in Faenza
PARKE-BERNET GALLERIES
November 12th 1960 $40,000 (£14,284)

St. Peter, from a set of Christ and Three Apostles symbolising the Three Ages of Man. Carved pinewood. Tyrol. End 15th century
DOROTHEUM
March 18th 1960 Sch. 100,000 (£1,350)

Important Mannerist boxwood carving of
Cleopatra by Baccio Bandinelli
(1493–1560) 16th century
SOTHEBY & CO
June 17th 1960 £620

Statuette of Neptune by Peter Vischer
the Elder. Nuremberg. 1st quarter of
the 16th century. Bronze
SOTHEBY & CO
October 14th 1960 £1,650

Hercules and Anteus Bronze School of
Giovanni da Bologna Late 16th
century
SOTHEBY & CO
October 14th 1960 £1,700

Honoré Daumier (1808–1879)
Ratapoil Bronze, cast by C. Valsuani
17½"
SOTHEBY & CO
July 6th 1960 £1,900

Edgar Degas (1834–1917)
Woman in an Armchair Bronze
H. 12½"
CHRISTIE, MANSON & WOODS, LTD
May 20th 1960 £1,680

Henri Matisse (1869–1954)
Deux Negresses Bronze Signed 1908
Stamp of caster, Valsuani 18½"
SOTHEBY & CO
July 7th 1960 £5,200

Pablo Picasso (b. 1881)
Buste d'un femme (Fernande Olivier)
Bronze Signed 14½"
SOTHEBY & CO
July 6th 1960 £3,200

Pablo Picasso (b. 1881)
Femme Accroupie Signed and dated 1902
SOTHEBY & CO
October 12th 1960 £48,000

Edouard Vuillard (1868–1940)
La Loge
PARKE-BERNET GALLERIES
26th October 1960 $51,000 (£11,072)

A fine and rare Ijaw carved wood figure
of a man seated on a stylised elephant.
26″. Niger Delta, taken at the Ekuri
Expedition, 1897
SOTHEBY & CO
June 27th 1960 £640

A fine Gandhara grey schist Buddha. 27″
3rd century A.D.
SOTHEBY & CO
December 12th 1960 £900

Henry Moore
Reclining Female Figure Alabaster
18½″ long
CHRISTIE, MANSON & WOODS, LTD
December 9th 1960 £5,775

A magnificent 16th-century Benin ivory pectoral
mask 10″ high, 5″ wide, 5″ deep.
Formerly in the collection of Dr R. Allman, C.M.G.
SOTHEBY & CO
June 27th 1960 £6,500

A Queen Anne long-case clock in fret-carved and inlaid mulberry wood, by Thomas Tompion, London. c. 1705
PARKE-BERNET GALLERIES
April 30th 1960 $4,250 (£1,518)

A fine Roman-striking month bracket clock with 8-inch dial, signed beneath the chapter ring, *Joseph Knibb, London,* and on the back-plate, *Joseph Knibb, Londini fecit.*   SOTHEBY & CO
December 9th 1960 £1,750

A fine Louis Quinze bronze and ormolu mantel-clock by J.-B. Baillou.
CHRISTIE, MANSON & WOODS, LTD
March 17th 1960 £1,575

A small double basket-top bracket clock signed by J. Windmills, London, with original oak travelling case. c. 1695
SOTHEBY & CO
December 9th 1960 £620

A fine Louis Quinze ormolu and Meissen porcelain clock, the movement by Filon à Paris, the group modelled by Kändler
CHRISTIE, MANSON & WOODS, LTD
November 24th 1960 £1,575

Thomas Tompion month long-case clock, No. 106, ten-inch dial, signed Tho. Tompion, Londini fecit. c. 1690
SOTHEBY & CO
May 13th 1960 £2,000

Claude Monet (1840–1926)
The Water Garden, Giverny: Evening
CHRISTIE, MANSON & WOODS, LTD
May 20th 1960 £19,950

A George III ormolu mantel-clock inset
with enamel plaques signed by W. H.
Craft c. 1794
PARKE-BERNET GALLERIES
May 6th 1960 $1,000 (£357)

An English walnut grandmother clock,
5′ 10″ high, by Daniel Quare, London.
Early 18th century
CHRISTIE, MANSON & WOODS, LTD
May 26th 1960 £995

A fine Louis Seize garniture de cheminée
in porcelain and ormolu in the manner
of Pierre Gouthière
SOTHEBY & CO
June 17th 1960 £1,000

A superb Russian gold presentation
snuff-box richly set with diamonds,
with the monogram of Czar Nicholas II,
by the Court Goldsmith, F. Köchli, St
Petersburg.
PARKE-BERNET GALLERIES
October 29th 1960 $5,500 (£1,964)

A Russian gold and opal parrot cage,
3¾″ high—by Carl Fabergé
CHRISTIE, MANSON & WOODS, LTD
March 1st 1960 £995

An important German Renaissance
pendant in the form of a mermaid.
5½″ South German. Late 16th century
SOTHEBY & CO
May 17th 1960 £3,400

Rock-crystal bonbonnière and cover
with the Arms of Catherine of Medici,
set with bands of enamelled gold.
3¾″ diameter
SOTHEBY & CO
May 17th 1960 £660

Fabergé Siberian jade elephant in
dark green, the tusks with gold mounts.
5″ long. In holly-wood case
SOTHEBY & CO
May 19th 1960 £500

Christ, SS. Nicholas and Alexander—an
Imperial tryptich ikon in jewelled gold
and enamel, by Fabergé. Date 1875
PARKE-BERNET GALLERIES
October 29th 1960 $1,600 (£571)

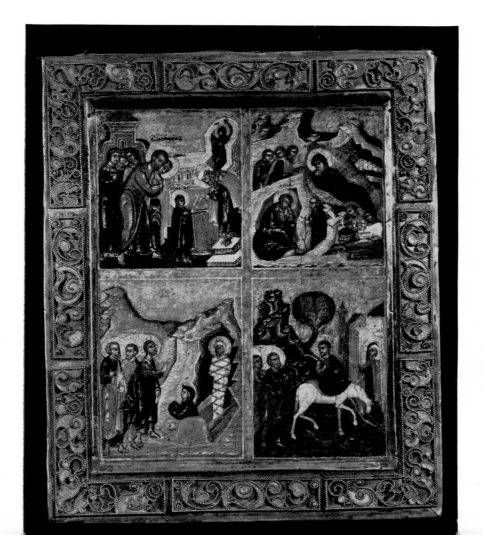

The Twelve Feasts of the Russian Ortho-
dox Church. Ikon. Stroganoff School.
Mid-16th century
CHRISTIE, MANSON & WOODS, LTD
April 26th 1960   £504

The Holy Vernicle; a gold and enamel
tryptich with the mark of K. Hahn,
St Petersburg. 19th century
PARKE-BERNET GALLERIES
October 29th 1960 $2,200 (£785)

A page from Fabergé's jewellery design
album, which contains about 850
original designs in colour
CHRISTIE, MANSON & WOODS, LTD
Album sold on April 5th 1960   £462

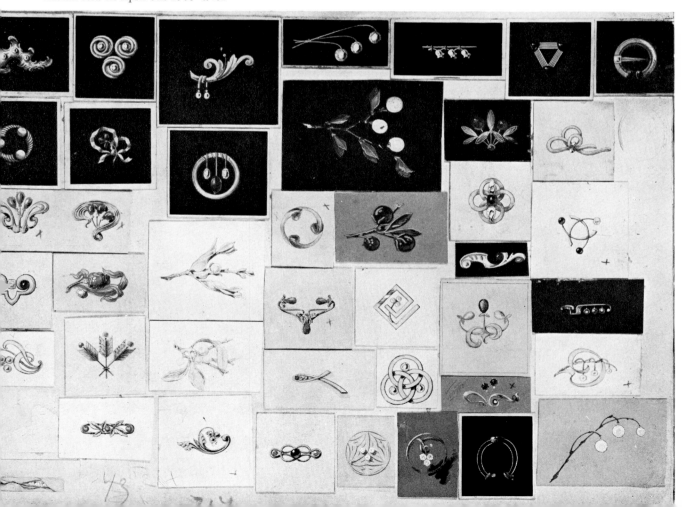

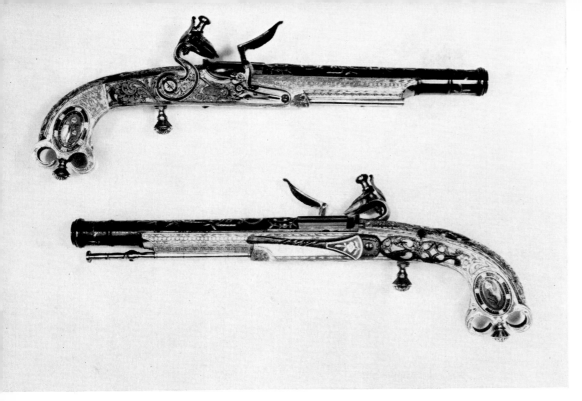

A pair of Scottish presentation flint-lock
pistols, by J. Murdoch. Last
quarter of the 18th century
CHRISTIE, MANSON & WOODS, LTD
June 21st 1960   £2,205

An important documentary enamel
plaque by C. F. Herold of the flight of
Stanislas Leczinski from Danzig in
1739. Inscribed: *Herold fecit, Alex
Fromery a Berlin.* 5⅛"
SOTHEBY & CO   July 11th 1960   £360

An important pair of Chinese hawks
painted in *famille rose* colours. Ch'ien
Lung period (1736–1795)
CHRISTIE, MANSON & WOODS, LTD
November 28th 1960 £7,560

A large wine-jar decorated with blue
underglaze. Chinese. Yüan dynasty.
14th century
CHRISTIE, MANSON & WOODS, LTD
June 27th 1960 £2,520

A fine ruby back Canton enamel saucer-
dish painted with Hsi Wang Mu, Royal
Mother of the West, and a handmaid
SOTHEBY & CO
July 12th 1960 £280

A spirited pottery model of a horse.
China. T'ang dynasty (618–906)
CHRISTIE, MANSON & WOODS, LTD
May 23rd 1960 £892

A large Imperial *cloisonné* incense
burner and cover from the Yuan Ming
Yuan Palace. 26½″ high. Ch'ien Lung
SOTHEBY & CO
October 18th 1960 £330

A chocolate-brown Coromandel lacquer
screen, the decoration mainly in white,
with reds, greens, and blues. Height 10′
Length 23′. Reign of the Emperor,
K'ang Hsi (1662–1722)
PARKE-BERNET GALLERIES
November 11th 1960 $6,750 (£2,409)

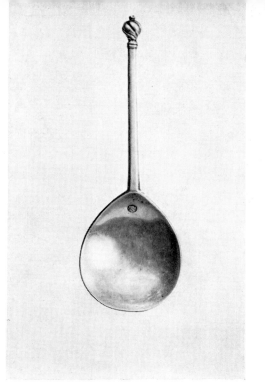

The Wilbraham cup, silver-gilt. 1585
CHRISTIE, MANSON & WOODS, LTD
June 22nd 1960 £2,700

A Henry VIII spoon of 1514
CHRISTIE, MANSON & WOODS, LTD
February 17th 1960 £1,050

The Great Seal of Ireland Cup, 1593.
Bought by the Belfast City Art Gallery
CHRISTIE, MANSON & WOODS, LTD
November 30th 1960 £7,000

The Pillaton Hall silver-gilt chalice and
paten, c. 1530. Unmarked
CHRISTIE, MANSON & WOODS, LTD
November 30th 1960 £5,000

A Norwegian pear-shaped coffee-pot.
Warden, M. A. Tank. Bergen. 1789
CHRISTIE, MANSON & WOODS, LTD
February 17th 1960 £700

A Queen Anne teapot, stand, and lamp by
John Leach, 1709. The Arms are those
of Bowes
CHRISTIE, MANSON & WOODS, LTD
November 30th 1960 £2,000

A George I octagonal pear-shaped teapot
by Simon Pantin, 1714
CHRISTIE, MANSON & WOODS, LTD
November 30th 1960 £1,400

A George II plain octagonal salver by
Pezé Pilleau, 1730
CHRISTIE, MANSON & WOODS, LTD
February 17th 1960 £1,250

An Irish plain bowl (1719), and dish
(1718), Dublin, maker David King
PHILLIPS, SON & NEALE
June 28th 1960   £500

A Charles II caudle cup of 1661
A *tazza* of the same date—both London
made
PARKE-BERNET GALLERIES
May 7th 1960 $900 (£321)
$1,000 (£357) respectively

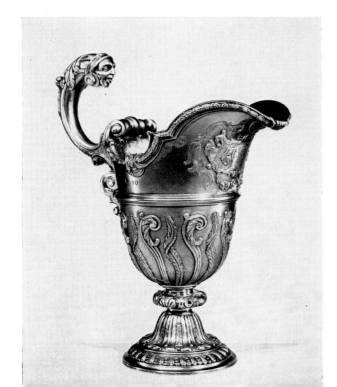

Fine George II silver-gilt sideboard ewer
by Paul de Lamerie, 14″ high. 1736
SOTHEBY & CO
November 17th 1960   £4,200

119

A Queen Anne silver-gilt Monteith by
John Gibbon, London, 1707
PARKE-BERNET GALLERIES
May 7th 1960 $2,700 (£964)

The cover of a William III silver-gilt
toilet casket by Pierre Harache, 1695,
the fine engraving probably by Simon
Gribelin
CHRISTIE, MANSON & WOODS, LTD
June 22nd 1960 £8,000

A George II engraved silver tray with
piecrust border by Jno. le Sage, London,
1738
PARKE-BERNET GALLERIES
May 7th 1960 $4,500 (£1,607)

One of a pair of Louis Quinze candle-
sticks by Michel Delapierre, Paris, 1752
CHRISTIE, MANSON & WOODS, LTD
May 25th 1960 £1,350

A Swedish parcel-gilt tankard by Arvard
Falck, Stockholm, 1691
CHRISTIE, MANSON & WOODS, LTD
June 22nd 1960 £1,150

A German parcel-gilt bowl and cover,
dated 1676. Perhaps Nürnberg
CHRISTIE, MANSON & WOODS, LTD
October 12th 1960 £819

A soup tureen from the Berkeley Castle
silver dinner service by Jacques
Roettiers, Paris, 1735-8. This, the finest
now existing, comprised 168 pieces
SOTHEBY & CO
June 16th 1960 £207,000

A carved walnut Armorial *credenza*,
Sienese, 16th century. From the *atelier*
of the sculptor, Barilli. The Arms are
those of the Chigi family
PARKE-BERNET GALLERIES
November 12th 1960 $1,100 (£393)

One of a matched pair of inlaid walnut
secretaire-cabinets with mirror doors,
made in London for Augustus the Strong
of Saxony. 18th century
PARKE-BERNET GALLERIES
May 7th 1960 $4,700 (£1,678)

A sculptured walnut *Stipo a Bambocci*,
Florentine, 16th century. Formerly in
the Lichtenstein Palace, Vienna
PARKE-BERNET GALLERIES
November 12th 1960 $750 (£268)

A Queen Anne walnut bureau with cross-banded borders, and boxwood stringing
PHILLIPS, SON & NEALE
December 13th 1960 £950

A Queen Anne walnut bureau-bookcase with mirror doors
PHILLIPS, SON & NEALE
February 16th 1960 £1,900

A George I inlaid walnut travelling kneehole-desk, with folding top. 18th century
PARKE-BERNET GALLERIES
April 29th 1960 $2,500 (£893)

A George II carved and gilded console, one of a pair. 18th century
PARKE-BERNET GALLERIES
May 7th 1960 $1,400 (£500) each

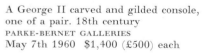

The settee from the Madingley Hall
suite, Queen Anne period, in carved,
gilt, wood covered with *rose petit point*.
18th century
April 30th 1960 $17,000 (£6,070)

A set of six George II walnut dining-
chairs with lion-paw feet, in brown
leather. c. 1745
PARKE-BERNET GALLERIES
May 7th 1960 $9,600 (£3,428)

A finely carved Chippendale mahogany
open armchair upholstered in Fulham
tapestry, once in the House of Lords.
18th century
PARKE-BERNET GALLERIES
May 7th 1960 $5,000 (£1,786)

One of an important set of six George I
walnut chairs
CHRISTIE, MANSON & WOODS, LTD
May 26th 1960 £1,260

Henri Matisse (1869–1954)
La Leçon de Peinture
CHRISTIE, MANSON & WOODS, LTD
May 20th 1960 £21,000

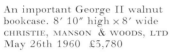

An important George II walnut
bookcase. 8′ 10″ high × 8′ wide
CHRISTIE, MANSON & WOODS, LTD
May 26th 1960   £3,780

A superb Chippendale serpentine silver-
table in carved mahogany. English or
Irish. 18th century
PARKE-BERNET GALLERIES
May 6th 1960 $2,500 (£893)

A Chippendale mahogany commode, the
top drawer enclosing a writing-slide
PHILLIPS, SON & NEALE
December 20th 1960   £760

A Chippendale mahogany tilting-top
tripod table with piecrust top. 18th
century
PARKE-BERNET GALLERIES
April 29th 1960 $4,500 (£1,607)

An important set of eight mahogany open armchairs by Thomas Chippendale the Younger
CHRISTIE, MANSON & WOODS, LTD
February 25th 1960 £5,775

A Chinese mirror-picture in a contemporary gilt-wood frame. Mid-18th century
CHRISTIE, MANSON & WOODS, LTD
February 25th 1960 £1,050

One of an important set of four Chinese Chippendale mahogany armchairs. Mid-18th century
CHRISTIE, MANSON & WOODS, LTD
May 26th 1960 £1,890

A pair of Chippendale open armchairs covered with Aubusson tapestry. 18th century
PARKE-BERNET GALLERIES
May 7th 1960 $4,000 (£1,428)

A very rare Chippendale fret-carved and brass-inlaid mahogany aviary. 18th century
PARKE-BERNET GALLERIES
April 30th 1960 $1,750 (£625)

A satinwood and inlaid bookcase with shelves and brass gallery, with tambour front
PHILLIPS, SON & NEALE
November 27th 1960 £1,200

A Louise Quinze commode of kingwood parquetry, *rouge* marble top. Stamped E. Doirat
PHILLIPS, SON & NEALE
December 6th 1960 £1,500

A Sheraton break-front secretaire-cabinet in inlaid satinwood and mahogany, inset with clock. Late 18th century
PARKE-BERNET GALLERIES
April 30th 1960 $4,250 (£1,605)

A Louis Quinze kingwood and tulipwood marquetry serpentine-fronted commode, mounted in *bronze doré*. Stamp of Nicholas Grevenich (ME 1768)
PARKE-BERNET GALLERIES
October 29th 1960 $8,500 (£3,036)

A Louis Quinze inlaid tulipwood and kingwood commode mounted with *bronze doré*, with the stamp of Adrien Faizelot-Delorme (ME 1748)
PARKE-BERNET GALLERIES
October 9th 1960 $4,750 (£1,697)

129

1 2   3   4

1. A fine Louis Quinze marquetry table
CHRISTIE, MANSON & WOODS, LTD
November 24th 1960   £2,835

2. Louis Quinze giltwood suite of seat
furniture signed I. Lebas.   Six armchairs, a pair of corner chairs of rare
form, and a pair of settees
SOTHEBY & CO
October 14th 1960   £3,600

3. An important Louis Quinze marquetry
table à ouvrage by J. F. Oeben
CHRISTIE, MANSON & WOODS, LTD
March 17th 1960   £13,650

4. Louis Seize marquetry Secretaire à
Abbatant, the front inlaid with a
picture of an Orangerie. Dark grey
marble top. 3′ 2″ wide
SOTHEBY & CO
June 17th 1960   £780

A fine small Louis Quinze *bureau plat*
by P. Migeon
CHRISTIE, MANSON & WOODS, LTD
March 17th 1960   £8,400

A Louis Quinze *vernis Martin* commode
CHRISTIE, MANSON & WOODS, LTD
November 24th 1960   £18,735

(*Left to right*) A Chelsea "Fable" scent-bottle
illustrating Aesop's Fable of the *Fox and
the Stork*, 4¼″, £500; a rare Chelsea
scent-bottle in the form of a monkey seated,
the head forming the stopper, 3¼″, £250;
a Chelsea Swan scent-bottle, the head and
neck forming the stopper, 3¼″, £520;
and a Chelsea peacock scent-bottle,
the head forming the stopper, 3½″, £300.
Otto and Magdalena Blohm Collection
SOTHEBY & CO
July 4th 1960

Fine and rare St Louis encased overlay
paperweight
SOTHEBY & CO
November 28th 1960 £700

1

2

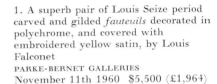

3

1. A superb pair of Louis Seize period carved and gilded *fauteuils* decorated in polychrome, and covered with embroidered yellow satin, by Louis Falconet
PARKE-BERNET GALLERIES
November 11th 1960 $5,500 (£1,964)

2. A pair of Louis Quinze period ormolu and Meissen porcelain candelabra
CHRISTIE, MANSON & WOODS, LTD
June 30th 1960 £1,575

3. One of a pair of 19th-century two-tier *encoignures* in the Empire style, with white marble tops
PHILLIPS, SON & NEALE
October 27th 1960 £1,500

4. An important pair of Louis Quinze ormolu wall-lights, 26½″ high
CHRISTIE, MANSON & WOODS, LTD
March 17th 1960 £1,995

5. Louis Quinze ormolu-mounted *blanc de chine* centrepiece 10″ high
SOTHEBY & CO
October 14th 1960 £1,550

5

4

An early Meissen bowl decorated with
chinoiserie figures. AR monogram
PHILLIPS, SON & NEALE
January 19th 1960 £600

A rare pair of du Paquier Vienna pilgrim
vases painted in *Schwarzlot* with
mythological subjects. c. 1730
CHRISTIE, MANSON & WOODS, LTD
November 14th 1960 £1,102

A Meissen group of the *Harlequin
Family*, modelled by J. J. Kandler,
c. 1740
CHRISTIE, MANSON & WOODS, LTD
May 2nd 1960 £1,417

A Louis Quinze period
ormolu and Meissen porcelain
candelabrum 18½″
CHRISTIE, MANSON & WOODS, LTD
July 1st 1960 £1,260

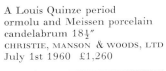

A rare and important enamel Limoges
enamel plaque of the Crucifixion, by the
so-called Monvaerni, on a convex copper
panel, with irregular purplish-black
counter enamel
SOTHEBY & CO
July 8th 1960 £1,900

An attractive Faenza *tazza* by the
Master of the Bergantini bowl, after
Raphael
SOTHEBY & CO
October 14th 1960   £540

An Urbino *istoriato* plate by Francesco
Xanto Avelli. 10″ diameter. c. 1530
SOTHEBY & CO
October 14th 1960   £110

A rare Chelsea coloured 'Goat and Bee'
jug. 4½″
SOTHEBY & CO
January 26th 1960   £350

A very rare early Chelsea group of
goats decorated by William Duesbury.
6½″
SOTHEBY & CO
May 10th 1960   £290

A pair of Nymphenburg
chinoiserie figures modelled by
Franz Anton Bustelli. c. 1760
CHRISTIE, MANSON & WOODS, LTD
November 14th 1960   £1,995

A French dessert service painted with
birds in natural floral settings
PHILLIPS, SON & NEALE
January 12th 1960 £540

A very rare Lambeth delft coloured
octagonal pill-slab with the Arms of the
Apothecaries' Company
SOTHEBY & CO
December 20th 1960 £580

Fine Künckel ruby glass beaker and
cover by Gottfried Spiller, the cover
carved in *hochschnitt*, the eleven-sided
body in *intaglio*
SOTHEBY & CO
December 9th 1960   £850

A fine lilac-ground Chamberlain's
Worcester jug, painted by Humphrey
Chamberlain. 9¾″ high. Mark in red
script
SOTHEBY & CO
November 8th 1960   £360

A very rare rococo coffee-pot and cover
with the impressed mark of Tebo. Bow.
10⅞″
SOTHEBY & CO
May 10th 1960   £250

The well-known Worcester coloured and
dated 'scratch cross' mug
SOTHEBY & CO
January 26th 1960   £720

An oval dish from a Worcester dessert service of 35 pieces, c. 1775, the painting probably by M. Soqui
CHRISTIE, MANSON & WOODS, LTD
November 14th 1960. Sold for a total of £1,449

A very fine Worcester basket, cover, and stand, blue scale ground, and yellow outlined basket moulding. 11″ Seal marks
SOTHEBY & CO
November 8th 1960 £450

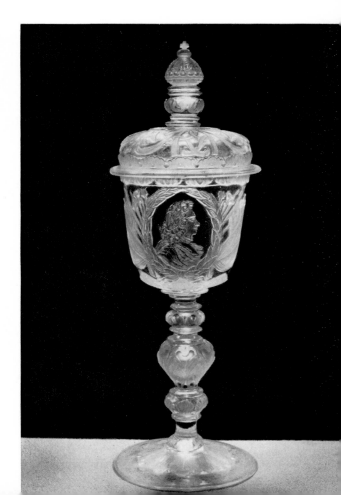

Magnificent early Petersdorf portrait goblet and cover by Friedrich Winter decorated in *hochschnitt* with a portrait of Augustus the Strong of Saxony. 14″ Late 17th century
SOTHEBY & CO
December 9th 1960 £900

A magnificent Imperial spinach-green jade
brush-washer carved with a continuous
mountain landscape. $7\frac{3}{8}''$ high, $8\frac{7}{8}''$ dia.
K'ang Hsi. With *cloisonné* and gilt metal stand
SOTHEBY & CO
October 18th 1960 £5,000

An important St Louis green overlay moulded
salamander weight
SOTHEBY & CO
November 28th 1960 £750

A very rare stippled goblet by David
Wolff
SOTHEBY & CO
June 16th 1960 £220

Fine enamelled Royal Armorial goblet
by Beilby, Newcastle-on-Tyne.
9¼″ c. 1762
SOTHEBY & CO
December 9th 1960
£1,820

Two engraved 'Privateer' glasses—one
'Success to the Eagle Frigate'—'John
Knill Commander' and the other
'Success to the Enterprize'
SOTHEBY & CO   October 21st 1960
£105 and £220 respectively

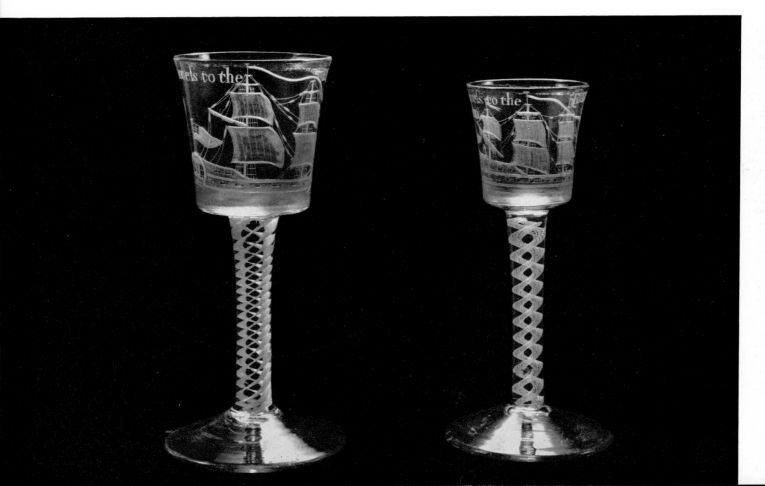

An Empire Aubusson carpet with a
lettuce green field. 14' 6" × 13' 3"
PARKE-BERNET GALLERIES
October 29th 1960 $1,750 (£624)

The Sheldon Tapestry Map of Oxford
and Berkshire c. 1647
SOTHEBY & CO
April 8th 1960   £4,200

The Triumph of Knowledge. Touraine
Gothic tapestry c. 1515
PARKE-BERNET GALLERIES
November 12th 1960 $16,000 (£5,713)

An important large Spanish needlework
carpet, 32' × 20' 18th century
CHRISTIE, MANSON & WOODS, LTD
June 30th 1960   £3,045

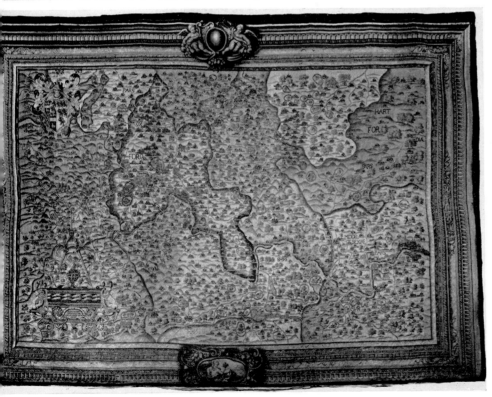

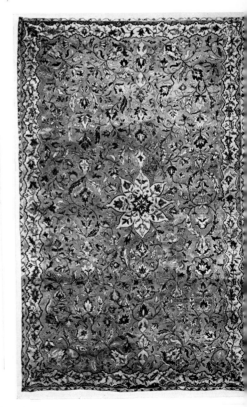

141.

One of a pair of attractive Louis Seize
entre fenêtre tapestry panels with scenes
from *Country Pleasures*; one marked
MRD. 7′ × 4′
SOTHEBY & CO
June 17th 1960 £1,000

One of a set of five panels of English
Mortlake tapestry
CHRISTIE, MANSON & WOODS, LTD
February 25th 1960 £2,940

A Tournai Gothic *millefleurs* Armorial
tapestry, c. 1495. The Arms are those of
Lord Dynham (d. 1501)
PARKE-BERNET GALLERIES
November 12th 1960 $32,500 (£11,605)

A Soho landscape tapestry by Paul
Saunders. Mid-18th century
SOTHEBY & CO
February 27th 1960   £900

A fine cut-silk Kashan prayer rug
woven for presentation to a Shah.
6′ 6″ × 3′ 11″
SOTHEBY & CO
June 17th 1960 £700

Rare Azerbaijan silk rug woven with
couplets praising the Sultan, Nader
Shah Afshar. Dated 1745
SOTHEBY & CO
February 26th 1960 £800

trade directory

AUCTION ROOMS

W. & F. C. Bonham & Sons Ltd,
  Montpelier Street, Knightsbridge, London, SW7 (Knightsbridge 9161)
Christie, Manson & Woods Ltd,
  8, King Street, St James's, London, SW1 (Trafalgar 9060)
Dorotheum Kunstabteilung,
  Dorotheergasse, 11, Wien, 1 (Telephone: 52 31 29; 52 79 78)
Galerie Charpentier,
  76, rue du Faubourg Saint-Honoré, Paris
Knight, Frank & Rutley,
  20, Hanover Square, London, W1 (Mayfair 37711)
Palais Galliéra,
  10, Avenue Pierre 1er. de Serbie, Paris
Parke-Bernet Galleries Inc.,
  980, Madison Avenue, New York, 21, N.Y (Trafalgar 9-8300)
Phillips, Son & Neale,
  Blenstock House, 7, Blenheim Street, New Bond Street, London, W1 (Mayfair 2424)
Sotheby & Co.,
  34/35, New Bond Street, London, W1 (Hyde Park 6545)

ASSOCIATIONS OF ART AND ANTIQUE DEALERS

Art and Antique Dealers' League of America, Inc.,
  237, East 60th Street, New York, 22, N.Y
The British Antique Dealers' Association Ltd,
  20, Rutland Gate, London, SW7
Bundesgremium des Handels mit Juwelen, Gold und Silberwaren, Uhren, Bildern,
  Antiquitäten und Kunstgegenstanden,
  Bauernmarkt, 13, Wien, I, Austria
Bundesverband des Deutschen Kunst und Antiquitätenhandels,
  Prinsenbau, Stuttgart, West Germany
Chambre Syndicale des Beaux Arts et de la Curiosité de Belgique,
  11, rue Saint Jean, Brussels, Belgium
Federazione Italiana Mercanti d'Arte,
  Piazza G., Gioacchino Belle 2, Rome, Italy
Syndicat National des Antiquaries, Négociants en Objets d'Art, tableaux anciens et
  modernes
  11, rue Jean Mermoz, Paris 8me, France
Vereeniging van Handelaren in Oude Kunst in Nederland,
  Leidsegracht, 48, Amsterdam, Holland

index

Antiquities

Arabia, Southern.   Alabaster frieze.   £315 ($882)   38
Assyria.   Marble relief.   £1,607 ($4,500)   44
,,   Relief.   £2,700 ($7,560)   25
Cyclades.   Marble figure.   £315 ($882)   38
Egypt.   Baboon (basalt).   £61 ($171)   22
,,   Cat (bronze).   £1,200 (13,360)   56
,,   Hawk (bronze).   £805 ($2,250)   44
,,   Osiris (basalt).   £980 ($2,744)   25
,,   ,,   (wood).   £270 ($756)   22
England.   Thurible of Godric.   £2,600 ($7,280)   32, *96*
Etruria.   Lion (limestone).   £110 ($308)   38
,,   Warrior (bronze).   £440 ($1,232)   25
Gandhara.   Buddha (grey schist).   £900 ($2,520)   56
Greece.   Krater, Attic red figure.   £1,000 ($2,800)   56
,,   ,,   ,,   ,,   £850 ($2,380)   56
,,   Lion (marble).   £893 ($2,500)   44
,,   Sphinx (bronze).   £400 ($1,120)   25
Ireland.   Gold bracelet.   £136 ($381)   38
Mexico.   Mask (marble).   £126 ($352)   38

Arms and Armour

Armet, Italian, 16th century.   £147 ($412)   47
Armour, suit, English.   £294 ($823)   47
,,   ,,   German.   £205 ($574)   47
Dagger, Swiss, 16th century.   £231 ($644)   47
Petronel, German.   £2,100 ($5,830)   59
Pistol, belt, Murdoch.   £420 ($1,176)   33
,,   Colt, London.   £190 ($532)   56
,,   ,,   ,,   £290 ($812)   59
,,   ,,   New York.   £440 ($1,232)   59
,,   flint-lock, Austrian.   £557 ($1,000)   29
,,   Freeman, J.   £115 ($322)   28
,,   Gasset à Paris.   £110 ($308)   28
,,   holster, Augsburg.   £152 ($426)   29
,,   ,,   Dutch.   £482 ($1,352)   29
,,   ,,   French.   £336 ($941)   29
,,   Saxon (1591).   £240 ($672)   40
,,   Scottish presentation.   £2,205 ($6,174)   33, *114*
,,   Silke, R.   £100 ($280)   28
,,   target, Pauly.   £240 ($672)   40
Rifle, revolving, Colt.   £480 ($1,344)   40
,,   sporting, German.   £121 ($338)   29
,,   ,,   ,,   £100 ($280)   28
,,   ,,   Greener.   £90 ($252)   28
Rocket-discharger.   £90 ($252)   28
Shield, parade, Italian.   £220 ($616)   47
Shot-gun, Jarré à Paris.   £120 ($336)   28
Sporting-gun, Wood, R.   £260 ($728)   40
Volley-gun.   £400 ($1,120)   40
,,   naval.   £142 ($398)   29

CERAMICS, EUROPEAN
Porcelain, English

Bow.   Actor and Actress.   £160 ($448)   28
,,   Bull and Cow.   £126 (1353)   46
,,   Coffee-pot.   £250 ($700)   29, *137*
,,   Dismal Hound.   £230 ($644)   28
,,   Erato.   £190 ($532)   19
,,   Gardener & Companion.   £330 ($924)   43
,,   Harlequin.   £170 ($476)   43
,,   Huntress.   £120 ($336)   43
,,   Scaramouche.   £700 ($1,960)   48
,,   Spring.   £190 ($532)   43
Chelsea.   Autumn.   £190 ($532)   43
,,   Spring.   £260 ($728)   43

Chelsea.   Summer.   £250 ($700)   43
,,   Winter.   £240 ($672)   43
,,   Bird.   £441 ($1,235)   46
,,   Candlestick groups.   £240 ($672)   28
,,   Cane-handle.   £140 ($392)   19
,,   Cup (triangle period).   £360 ($1,008)   28
,,   Dish, sunflower.   £240 ($672)   28
,,   Goats.   £290 ($812)   28, *135*
,,   Guan.   £735 ($2,058)   46
,,   Jug, 'Goat & Bee'.   £350 ($980)   19, *135*
,,   Melon tureen.   £580 ($1,624)   59
,,   Miniature figures:
      gallant.   £150 ($420)   43
      ,,   ,,   ,,   43
      ,,   and companion.   £145 ($406)   43
      highlander.   £150 ($420)   43
      hunter.   £250 ($700)   43
      poet.   £145 ($406)   43
      putti.   £48 ($134)   43
      Shepherd and shepherdess.   £320 ($896)   43
,,   Nourrice, La.   £609 ($1,705)   46
,,   Plates, 'Hans Sloane'.   £220 ($616)   19
,,   ,,   ,,   ,,   £200 ($560)   19
,,   ,,   ,,   ,,   £260 ($728)   19
,,   Scent bottles, Fable.   £500 ($1,400)   *131*
,,   ,,   Monkey.   £250 ($700)   *131*
,,   ,,   Swan.   £520 ($1,456)   *131*
,,   ,,   Peacock.   £300 ($840)   *131*
,,   Seasons.   £980 ($2,744)   48
,,   Shepherdess.   £199 ($557)   46
,,   Tyrolese Dancers.   £273 ($764)   46
,,   ,,   £3,600 ($10,080)   51
Chelsea-Derby.   Abelard & Heloise.   £300 ($840)   19
,,   Nuns.   £300 ($840)   19
Derby.   Cabaret.   £310 ($868)   28
,,   Dish.   £110 ($308)   19
,,   Jardinière.   £200 ($560)   28
,, , Bloor.   Vases.   £310 ($868)   59
English.   Bowl.   £130 ($364)   28
Longton Hall.   Leaf dishes.   £230 ($644)   43
,,   Salts, shell.   £120 ($336)   43
,,   Winter.   £140 ($392)   19
Spode.   Vases.   £120 ($336)   43
Swansea.   Dessert service.   £620 ($1,736)   60
,,   Dish.   £130 ($364)   43
,,   Plates.   £190 ($532)   43
Worcester.   Baskets, pierced.   £150 ($420)   29
,,   ,,   ,,   £490 ($1,372)   29
,,   ,,   ,,   £540 ($1,512)   29
,,   ,,   ,,   £360 ($1,008)   43
,,   ,,   ,,   £430 ($1,204)   43, *138*
,,   Bough pots.   £400 ($1,120)   28
,,   Chocolate cup and saucer.   £600 ($1,680)   48
,,   Cup and saucer.   £155 ($434)   46
,,   ,,   £185 ($518)   19
,,   Dish, O'Neale.   £210 ($588)   19
,,   Dishes.   £250 ($700)   19
,,   Dessert service.   £1,449 ($4,057)   *138*
,,   Jug.   £290 ($812)   19
,,   Junket dish.   £520 ($1,456)   19
,,   Mug.   £720 ($2,016)   19, *137*
,,   Plate.   £190 ($532)   19
,,   ,,   (Gloucester).   £310 ($868)   28
,,   ,,   ,,   £200 ($560)   28
,,   ,,   ,,   £420 ($1,176)   19
,,   ,,   £210 ($588)   19
,,   ,,   O'Neale.   £190 ($532)   19
,,   Sauceboats.   £115 ($322)   19

Worcester.	Sauce tureen. £540 ($1,512)		19
,,	Sucrier, pencilled. £62 ($174)		19
,,	Teapot. £620 ($1,708)		19
,,	,, £310 ($868)		29
,,	Vases. £130 ($364)		19
,,	,, £195 ($546)		28
,, , Chamberlains.	Jug. £360 ($1,008)		*137*
,, , Flight, Barr & Barr.	Dessert Service. £115 ($434)		59
,, ,, ,,	Dinner service. £420 ($1,176)		59
,, ,, ,,	Vases. £200 ($560)		28
,, ,, ,,	,, £125 ($350)		59

Porcelain, Continental

Chantilly.	Bowls. £260 ($728)		26
,,	,, £85 ($238)		26
,,	Plate. £219 ($608)		52
Doccia.	Francis I. £230 ($644)		26
Mennecy.	Bonbonnière. £240 ($672)		43
Paris.	Dessert service. £280 ($784)		59
,,	,, ,, £540 ($1,512)		136
,,	Vases. £200 ($560)		59
Sèvres.	Cachepots. £1,531 ($4,287)		52
,,	Plates. £729 ($2,041)		52
,,	Tureen. £4,154 ($11,631)		52
,,	Vases. £1,102 ($3,086)		46
,,	,, £630 ($1,764)		46
,,	Louis Quinze. £153 ($428)		52
,,	Mme du Barry. £241 ($675)		52
,,	Pygmalion. £226 ($633)		52
Tournai.	Jardinière. £210 ($588)		26
Vincennes.	Cachepots. £400 ($1,120)		26
,,	Cup & saucer. £1,182 ($3,310)		52
,,	Les Mangeurs de Raisin. £2,100 ($5,830)		51
,,	Vase. £400 ($1,120)		43
Frankenthal.	Chinoiserie figure. £120 ($336)		26
,,	Group, Melchior. £150 ($420)		43
,,	Lady & gentleman. £252 ($706)		46
,,	Merchant & wife. £231 ($647)		46
Fürstenberg.	Miner. £85 ($238)		26
Höchst.	Columbine. £130 ($364)		26
,,	Der Bekräntze Schläfer. £380 ($1,064)		51
,,	Disturbed Slumber. £400 ($1,120)		51
,,	Girl milking a goat. £280 ($784)		51
,,	Sultan & Sultana. £185 ($518)		26
Meissen.	Bowl, chinoiserie. £300 ($840)		43
,,	,, ,, £600 ($1,680)	60,	*133*
,,	,, river scenes. £340 ($952)		43
,,	Cats (pair) £1,700 ($4,760)		51
,,	Chinaman & companion. £399 ($1,117)		46
,,	Dancing Harlequin. £460 ($1,288)		59
,,	Fishwife. £155 ($434)		26
,,	Goblet and cover. £370 ($1,036)		26
,,	Group, Italian Comedy. £2,000 ($5,600)		51
,,	Harlequin. £130 ($364)		25
,,	Kennel. £160 ($443)		43
,,	Lovers. £250 ($700)		26
,,	Musicians. £1,150 ($3,220)		51
,,	Oriental woman. £273 ($764)		46
,,	Peasant Lovers. £3,200 ($8,960)		51
,,	Pierrot. £300 ($840)		26
,,	Scaramouche & Columbine. £800 ($2,240)		26
,,	,, ,, £500 ($1,400)		26
,,	Snuff-box. £1,700 ($4,760)		51
,,	Spirit-barrel. £588 ($1,646)		46
,,	Stürmische Liebhaber. £580 ($1,624)		26

Meissen.	Sugar-box. £115 ($322)		26
,,	,, £160 ($443)		43
,,	Sultan on elephant. £3,600 ($10,800)		51
,,	Tankard. £92 ($258)		25
,,	Toilet-jars. £410 ($1,148)		43
,,	Tureen & stand. £100 ($280)		59
Nymphenburg.	Chinoiserie figures. £1,995 ($5,586)	46,	*135*
,,	Pilgrim. £210 ($583)		43
,,	Seasons. £260 ($728)		26
Vienna.	Pilgrim vases. £1,102 ($3,086)	46,	*133*

Pottery, English

Astbury-Whieldon.	Actor. £100 ($280)		59
Lambeth.	Dish. £480 ($1,344)		59
,,	Pill-slab. £580 ($1,624)	59,	*136*
Liverpool.	Flower-holders. £115 ($322)		59
Saltglaze.	Teapot. £95 ($266)		59
Toby jugs:			
	Astbury-Whieldon. £52 ($146)		21
	Wood, Enoch. £60 ($168)		21
	Wood, Ralph. £40 ($112)		21
	,, ,, Miniature. £58 ($162)		21
	Whieldon. £42 ($118)		21
Whieldon.	Dovecot. £210 ($583)		59
Wood, Ralph.	Bacchus jug. £34 ($95)		21
,, ,,	Prince Hal jug. £220 ($616)		21
,, ,,	Sweep. £60 ($168)		59

Pottery, Continental

Castel Durante.	Dish. £42 ($118)		42
Castelli.	Plaque. £170 ($476)		43
,,	,, £60 ($168)		42
,,	,, £85 ($238)		42
Chagall, M.	Automne. £2,438 ($6,826)		53
Faenza.	Drug jar. £65 ($182)		42
,,	Tazza. £540 ($1,512)		135
Gauguin, P.	Jardinière. £582 ($1,630)		55
German.	Jug, stoneware. £280 ($784)		54
,,	,, ,, £260 ($728)		54
Marseilles.	Dish. £75 ($210)		42
Montelupo	,, £35 ($98)		42
,,	,, £58 ($162)		42
,,	,, £58 ($162)		42
,,	,, £56 ($157)		42
Niderviller.	Peasant. £48 ($134)		42
Proskau.	Partridge tureen. £150 ($420)		59
Rouault, G.	Baigneuse. £1,094 ($,063)		55
Talavera.	Dish. £30 ($84)		43
Toulouse-Lautrec, H. de.	Yvette Guilbert. £1,714 ($4,799)		56
Urbino.	Plate. £110 ($308)		135

Clocks, Watches, Barometers, etc.

Barometer.	Quare, London. £280 ($784)		21
Clock, bracket.	Asselin, London. £400 ($1,120)		54
,, ,,	Colston. £230 ($644)		54
,, ,,	Constantin. £300 ($840)		54
,, ,,	Etherington. £600 ($1,680)		54
,, ,,	Jones, Henry. £480 ($1,344)		54
,, ,,	Knibb, John. £850 ($2,380)		54
,, ,,	Knibb, Joseph. £1,750 ($4,900)	54,	*106*
,, ,,	,, ,, £950 ($2,660)		54
,, ,,	Windmills. £620 ($1,736)	54,	*107*
,,	bronze & ormolu. £1,575 ($4,410)		106
,,	cartel. Louis XV. £650 ($1,820)		33
,,	gilt bronze. Louis XV. £2,310 ($6,468)		59

Clock, grandmother, Quare. £995 ($2,786)	109
,, long case. Cattell, London. £420 ($1,176)	54
,, ,, Knibb, John. £1,650 ($4,570)	54
,, ,, Tompion. £1,518 ($4,250)	106
,, ,, ,, £2,000 ($5,600)	107
,, mantel, George III. £357 ($1,000)	109
,, ormolu. Le Roy. £3,000 ($8,400)	54
,, ,, Louis XV £600 ($1,680)	54
,, ormolu & porcelain. £1,995 ($5,586)	36
,, ,, ,, £,575 ($4,410)	107
,, perpetual motion, Cox. £600 ($1,680)	54
,, table, Austria. £142 ($398)	54
Watches. Arnold, J. R. £131 ($367)	20
,, Beronneau, F. £399 ($1,117)	20
,, Berthaud, F. £105 ($294)	20
,, Bertram, W. £126 ($353)	20
,, Bordier. £105 ($294)	20
,, Bréguet. £178 ($498)	20
,, ,, £577 ($1,616)	20
,, ,, £126 ($353)	20
,, ,, £231 ($647)	20
,, ,, £105 ($294)	20
,, ,, £220 ($616)	20
,, ,, £357 ($1,000)	20
,, Cummins, T. £126 ($353)	20
,, Dunlop, A. £65 ($182)	20
,, Dupont, London. £126 ($353)	20
,, Earnshaw, T. £142 ($398)	20
,, Oudin, J. £178 ($498)	20
,, Tompion, T. £57 ($160)	20
,, ,, £756 ($2,119)	20

Furniture, English

Armchairs, Chippendale. £1,250 ($3,500)	27
,, ,, £1,890 ($5,292)	30, *127*
,, ,, £3,748 ($10,500)	44
,, ,, £1,786 ($5,000)	27, *124*
,, ,, £1,071 ($3,000)	27
,, ,, £1,428 ($4,000)	27, *127*
,, ,, £1,000 ($2,800)	27
,, ,, £220 ($616)	53
,, ,, £892 ($2,498)	53
,, Hepplewhite. £787 ($2,204)	53
,, ,, £1,220 ($3,416)	60
,, mahogany. £5,775 ($16,170)	20, *127*
,, Adam. £3,780 ($10,584)	29
,, walnut. £651 ($1,823)	30
,, ,, £504 ($1,411)	30
Andirons, Regency. £42 ($118)	53
Aviary, Chippendale. £606 ($1,750)	27, *127*
Bookcase. £1,200 ($3,360)	128
,, Regency. £609 ($1,705)	42
,, walnut. £3,780 ($10,584)	30, *126*
Buffet, James I. £179 ($500)	44
Bureau. £950 ($2,660)	123
Bureau-bookcase. £1,900 (5,320)	60, *123*
Cabinet, Adam. £1,071 ($3,000)	27
,, Chippendale. £2,320 ($6,500)	27
,, lacquer. £1,680 ($2,646)	30
,, red lacquer. £720 ($2,016)	53
,, writing. £1,680 ($4,704)	30
Chairs, Chippendale. £1,714 ($4,800)	44
,, dining. £3,428 ($9,600)	27, *124*
,, Queen Anne. £560 ($1,568)	21
,, ,, ,, £609 ($1,705)	30
,, ,, ,, £624 ($1,750)	44
,, walnut. £1,928 ($5,400)	27

Chairs, walnut. £1,928 ($5,400)	124
Chest, Tudor. £179 ($500)	44
Commode, Chippendale. £2,320 ($6,500)	27
,, ,, ,, £2,857 ($8,000)	27
,, ,, ,, £735 ($2,058)	30
,, ,, ,, £760 ($2,128)	60, *126*
,, marquetry. £1,470 ($4,116)	42
,, Sheraton. £945 ($2,646)	21
Desk, knee-hole. £892 ($8,498)	53, *123*
,, partners. £1,786 ($5,000)	27
Fender, Regency. £105 ($294)	53
Kettle-stand, Chippendale. £409 ($1,145)	42
,, ,, £273 ($764)	53
Mirrors, gilt, George II. £441 ($1,235)	29
,, ,, ,, £399 ($1,117)	53
,, rococo. £420 ($1,176)	59
Secretaire, Adam-Chippendale. £1,071 ($3,000)	27
,, Chippendale. £1,250 ($3,500)	27
,, George I. £1,606 ($4,500)	27
,, Queen Anne. £1,678 ($4,700)	27, *122*
,, Sheraton. £1,605 ($4,250)	27, *129*
Settee, Hepplewhite. £1,339 ($3,750)	27
,, George I. £536 ($1,500)	44
Settees, armchairs, Adam. £3,780 ($10,584)	29
Sideboard, Adam. £520 ($1,456)	59
Suite, The Madingley Hall. £6,070 ($17,000)	27, *124*
Table, breakfast. £231 ($647)	53
,, card. £945 ($2,646)	30
,, ,, £1,000 ($2,800)	47
,, console. £1,606 ($4,500)	27
,, ,, £1,522 ($4,262)	29
,, ,, £500 ($1,400)	123
,, library. £1,517 ($4,250)	27
,, ,, £2,142 ($6,000)	27
,, marquetry. £756 ($2,117)	29
,, Pembroke. £504 ($1,411)	42
,, ,, £600 ($1,680)	47
,, ,, £400 ($1,120)	60
,, Sheraton. £700 ($1,960)	60
,, side. £210 ($583)	53
,, ,, £600 ($1,680)	60
,, ,, £820 ($2,296)	60
,, silver. £893 ($2,500)	126
,, tripod. £1,606 ($4,500)	27, *126*
,, writing. £525 ($1,470)	53
,, ,, £378 ($1,058)	42
,, ,, £1,155 ($3,234)	42
,, ,, £210 ($583)	53
Torchères, Chippendale. £1,102 ($3,086)	30
Wall-lights, Regency. £378 ($1,058)	53

Furniture, Continental

Dutch. Commode. £270 ($756)	22
,, Vitrine. £338 ($946)	22
French. Armoire. £912 ($2,554)	31
,, Armchairs. £948 ($2,654)	31
,, ,, £636 ($1,781)	50
,, ,, £1,417 ($3,968)	36
,, Boiserie. £4,000 ($11,200)	53
,, ,, £2,479 ($6,941)	52
,, ,, £3,208 ($8,982)	52
,, Bonheur du jour. £820 ($2,296)	53
,, Bureau. £2,005 ($5,715)	56
,, Bureau plat. £8,400 ($23,520)	22, *130*
,, Cabinets. £2,041 ($5,715)	31
,, Canapé. £3,748 ($10,500)	44
,, Candelabra. £1,281 ($3,587)	36
,, ,, £1,575 ($4,410)	36, *131*

French.	Candelabra.	£1,312 ($3,674)	36
,,	,,	£3,150 ($8,820)	47
,,	,,	£2,520 ($7,056)	47
,,	Centrepiece.	£1,550 ($4,340)	132
,,	Chairs.	£955 ($2,674)	50
,,	,,	£3,934 ($11,015)	52
,,	,,	£2,835 ($7,938)	48
,,	Chaise longue.	£1,680 ($4,704)	36
,,	Chenets.	£441 ($1,235)	47
,,	Commode.	£250 ($700)	60
,,	,,	£1,531 ($4,287)	31
,,	,,	£1,500 ($4,200)	60, 128
,,	,,	£1,500 ($4,200)	33
,,	,,	£1,248 ($3,494)	56
,,	,,	£3,000 ($8,400)	33
,,	,,	£6,300 ($17,640)	48
,,	,,	£2,282 ($6,390)	50
,,	,,	£2,224 ($6,227)	50
,,	,,	£773 ($2,164)	56
,,	,,	£580 ($1,624)	60
,,	,,	£9,975 ($21,930)	48
,,	,,	£18,375 ($51,450)	48, 130
,,	,,	£3,036 ($8,500)	129
,,	,,	£1,697 ($4,750)	129
,,	Consoles-dessertes.	£3,780 ($10,584)	48
,,	Desk.	£2,296 ($6,429)	50
,,	Encoignures.	£520 ($1,456)	60
,,	,,	£1,200 ($3,300)	33
,,	,,	£1,458 ($4,082)	52
,,	,,	£1,500 ($4,200)	132
,,	Fauteuils.	£1,963 ($5,500)	44, 131
,,	,,	£7,860 ($22,008)	36
,,	Garniture.	£1,000 ($2,800)	110
,,	Guéridon.	£4,449 ($12,457)	52
,,	,,	£2,100 ($5,830)	54
,,	,,	£11,070 ($30,996)	52
,,	Kennel.	£5,468 ($15,310)	52
,,	Seat furniture.	£3,600 ($10,080)	130
,,	Secretaire.	£2,005 ($5,614)	56
,,	,,	£780 ($2,184)	33, 130
,,	,,	£2,100 ($5,880)	33
,,	Semainier.	£970 ($2,716)	50
,,	Settee.	£1,458 ($4,082)	31
,,	Suite.	£1,100 ($3,080)	31
,,	Table.	£17,139 ($47,990)	52
,,	,,	£1,995 ($5,586)	48
,,	,,	£2,835 ($7,938)	48, 130
,,	,,	£2,041 ($5,715)	56
,,	,,	£2,442 ($7,146)	31
,,	,,	£2,552 ($7,146)	52
,,	,,	£2,552 ($7,145)	52
,,	,, à ouvrage.	£1,785 ($8,232)	36
,,	,, ,,	£13,650 ($36,540)	22, 130
,,	,, side.	£500 ($1,400)	60
,,	,, tray-top.	£480 ($1,344)	60
,,	,, writing.	£1,050 ($2,940)	33
,,	,, ,,	£2,940 ($8,232)	36
,,	,, ,,	£35,700 ($99,960)	22
,,	,, ,,	£1,509 ($4,225)	56
,,	Torchère, bronze.	£948 ($2,766)	51
,,	Vitrine.	£6,200 ($17,360)	33
,,	,,	£734 ($2,005)	31
,,	Wall-lights.	£2,835 ($7,938)	47
,,	,,	£714 ($1,999)	47
,,	,,	£1,365 ($3,822)	36
,,	,,	£1,837 ($5,147)	47
,,	,,	£1,995 ($5,586)	132
,,	Work-table.	See: Table à ouvrage.	

German.	Tabourets.	£1,500 ($4,200)	44
Italy.	Credenza.	£321 ($900)	45
,,	,,	£393 ($1,100)	45, 122
,,	Stipi à bambocci.	£268 ($750)	45, 122
,,	,, ,,	£250 ($700)	45
,,	Table. ,,	£286 ($800)	45
Spain.	,,	£357 ($1,000)	45

Glass

Ale glass, engraved.	£48 ($134)	31
Beaker, engraved, German.	£380 ($1,064)	54
,, Potsdam.	£850 ($2,380)	54, 137
Decanter, engraved, Jacobite.	£145 ($406)	45
Goblet, Anti-Gallican Society.	£160 ($443)	54
,, basket-twist.	£140 ($392)	54
,, enamelled, Beilby.	£1,820 ($5,096)	54, 140
,, engraved.	£68 ($190)	31
,, Petersdorf.	£900 ($2,520)	54, 138
,, Wolff.	£220 ($616)	31, 140
Scounces, George III, Waterford.	£1,000 ($2,800)	27
Sweetmeat.	£62 ($174)	31
Wine-glass, coloured twist.	£74 ($207)	31
,, ,,	£56 ($157)	31
,, ,,	£50 ($140)	31
,, engraved.	£160 ($443)	46
,, ,,	£145 ($406)	54
,, ,,	£105 ($294)	140
,, ,,	£220 ($616)	140
,, ,, Jacobite.	£230 ($644)	45

Glass Paperweights

Baccarat, bouquet.	£310 ($868)	48
,, flower.	£115 ($322)	48
,, millefiore, close.	£180 ($504)	48
,, millefiore, scattered.	£150 ($420)	48
,, overlay, green flash.	£225 ($630)	48
,, pear.	£160 ($443)	48
,, Queen Victoria.	£210 ($583)	48
,, snake.	£340 ($952)	48
Clichy, bouquet.	£210 ($583)	48
,, double overlay, turquoise.	£440 ($1,232)	48
St Louis, animal silhouette.	£175 ($490)	48
,, bouquet.	£260 ($728)	48
,, carpet ground.	£260 ($728)	48
,, crown.	£190 ($532)	48
,, ,,	£200 ($560)	48
,, flower.	£150 ($420)	48
,, grapevine.	£165 ($457)	48
,, mushroom.	£190 ($532)	48
,, overlay, pink encased.	£700 ($1,960)	48, 131
,, salamander.	£720 ($2,100)	48, 139

Miniatures

Bogle, J. Commodore Johnstone.	£178 ($498)	20
Cleyn, P. King James II.	£273 ($764)	20
Cooper, A. Elizabeth Stuart and Frederick of the Palatinate.	£273 ($764)	20
Cooper, S. Cromwell, Bridget.	£399 ($1,117)	20
,, ,, Richard.	£204 ($571)	20
,, Chadwick, Katherine.	£315 ($882)	20
,, Charles II.	£525 ($1,470)	20
,, Duchess of Buckingham.	£346 ($969)	20
Cosway, R. Lord Henry Fitzgerald.	£157 ($440)	20
Cross, L. Queen Anne.	£336 ($941)	20
Engleheart, J. D. C. Miss Lucy Engleheart.	£147 ($412)	20
Hilliard, N. Anne, Queen of Denmark.	£399 ($1,117)	20

Isabey, J.-B. Hortense, Queen of Holland. £294 ($823) — 19
,, Napoleon I. £756 ($2,117) — 33
Nattier, J. M. La Comtesse du Barry. £115 ($322) — 19
Oliver, I. James I. £294 ($823) — 20
Oliver, P. Arabella Stuart. £262 ($733) — 20
Parant, L.-B. Napoleon I. £315 ($882) — 33
Petitot, J. Lady Catherine Howard. £2,552 ($7,146) — 33
,, Louis Seize. £115 ($322) — 19
,, Mlle de la Vallière. £231 ($647) — 46
Plimer, A. George Bolsom. £120 ($336) — 20
,, Sarah Martin. £210 ($588) — 20
Sicardi, L. Louis Seize. £178 ($498) — 19
Smart, John. Beckford, Mrs William. £152 ($436) — 20
,, Campbell, Mrs. £304 ($851) — 20
,, Macartney, Lord. £105 ($294) — 19
,, Mexboro', Earl of. £115 ($322) — 20
,, Mohammed Ali Khan. £304 ($851) — 20
,, Townsend, Mrs Samuel £231 ($647) — 20
Zincke, C. Princess Sobieski. £115 ($322) — 19

Objets d'Art
Badge, hat, Italian. £750 ($2,100) — 29
Biberon, rock crystal. £210 ($558) — 33
Blackamoors, Venetian. £370 ($1,036) — 36
Bonbonnière. £1,350 ($3,780) — 49
,, £660 ($1,848) — 111
Box, gold, English. £220 ($660) — 33
,, ,, Fabergé. £2,000 ($5,600) — 58
,, ,, ,, £600 ($1,680) — 60
,, ,, with miniature. £1,550 ($4,340) — 49
,, ,, ,, ,, £231 ($647) — 46
,, ,, ,, ,, £315 ($882) — 33
,, ,, Swedish. £777 ($2,176) — 33
,, ,, Swiss. £126 $353) — 30
,, ,, ,, £231 ($647) — 30
Cage, bird-. £920 ($2,576) — 58
Cage, parrot, Fabergé. £995 ($2,786) — 111
Casket, enamel, Battersea. £1,700 ($4,760) — 49
,, Spanish. £714 ($1,999) — 46
Chess-set, Fabergé. £1,500 ($4,200) — 58
Cross, enamel, Limoges. £720 ($2,016) — 59
Design Album, Fabergé. £462 ($1,294) — 113
Easter egg, Fabergé. £2,400 ($6,720) — 49
Elephant jade, Fabergé. £500 ($1,400) — 111
Enamel plaque, Herold. £360 ($1,008) — 114
,, Limoges. £1,900 ($5,320) — 37, 134
Ewers, Tortoiseshell. £840 ($2,352) — 46
Icon, N. Russian School. £89 ($249) — 25
,, St George. £168 ($470) — 25
,, Stroganoff School. £504 ($1,411) — 25, 112
,, Three Saints. £168 ($470) — 25
,, Imperial Tryptich. £571 ($1,600) — 112
,, Tryptich, K. Hahn. £785 ($2,200) — 113
Inkwell, Fabergé. £399 ($1,117) — 33
Jewel-case, marquetry. £3,791 ($10,615) — 52
Nautilus shell, mounted. £420 ($1,176) — 46
Ostrich cup. £131 ($367) — 25
Parasol handle, Fabergé. £84 ($235) — 25
,, ,, ,, £136 ($381) — 25
Paste-pot, Fabergé. £336 ($941) — 30
Patch-box, Fabergé. £157 ($440) — 33
,, ,, £220 ($616) — 33
Pendant, Augsburg. £950 ($2,660) — 29
,, cameo, Italian. £2,600 ($7,280) — 29
,, dragon, Spanish. £1,100 ($3,080) — 49
,, German. £5,800 ($16,240) — 49

Pendant, German. £2,000 ($5,600) — 29
,, ,, £3,400 ($9,520) — 29, 111
,, nef, Venetian. £2,400 ($6,720) — 29
,, S. German. £2,400 ($6,720) — 49
,, Spanish. £1,050 ($2,940) — 29
Pillars, marble, 14th century. £2,041 ($5,715) — 56
Snuff-box, agate. £283 ($792) — 46
,, gold. £3,200 (8,960) — 49
,, ,, £2,750 ($7,700) — 49
,, ,, £2,800 ($7,840) — 49
,, Russian. £2,000 ($5,500) — 110
Vase, gold & enamel. £5,000 ($14,000) — 48
,, marble, Clodion. £481 ($1,347) — 52
Violin, Antonio, Milan. £504 ($1,411) — 30
,, Guadignini. £1,150 ($3,194) — 59

Oriental Works of Art
Amber boulder. £160 ($443) — 41
,, brush-washer. £240 ($672) — 41
,, Eight Immortals. £520 ($1,456) — 41
,, peach bowl. £400 ($1,120) — 41
Bronze Boddhisattva. £114 ($319) — 58
,, chüeh. £550 ($1,540) — 24
,, mules' heads. £4,800 ($13,440) — 24
Ceramics,
Chinese. Bowl, Chêng Tê. £380 ($1,064) — 24
,, ,, Chün. £155 ($434) — 58
,, ,, K'ang Hsi. £210 ($583) — 58
,, ,, leaf-form. £423 ($1,184) — 50
,, ,, Northern celadon. £740 ($2,072) — 38
,, ,, ,, £1,200 ($3,360) — 38
,, ,, ,, £1,100 ($3,080) — 38
,, ,, turquoise. £604 ($1,691) — 50
,, ,, ,, £473 ($1,324) — 50
,, ,, underglaze red. £450 ($1,260) — 40
,, ,, ,, £290 ($812) — 58
,, ,, Yung Chêng. £340 ($952) — 58
,, Bulb bowl, celadon. £320 ($896) — 38
,, Cat. £460 ($1,288) — 50
,, Cocks. £2,989 ($8,369) — 50
,, Conch-shell box. £656 ($1,837) — 50
,, Dinner service. £925 ($2,590) — 40
,, ,, £660 ($1,848) — 58
,, Dish. £1,200 ($3,360) — 24
,, ,, £220 ($616) — 58
,, ,, £800 ($2,240) — 58
,, ,, celadon. £400 ($1,120) — 38
,, ,, ,, £290 ($812) — 38
,, ,, leaf-form. £425 ($1,246) — 50
,, Dogs, pair. £640 ($1,792) — 50
,, Ducks. £1,531 ($4,287) — 50
,, Equestrienne figure. £200 ($560) — 58
,, Ewers as chickens. £460 ($1,224) — 50
,, Ewer, kinuta. £540 ($1,512) — 38
,, ,, £165 ($457) — 58
,, Hawks. £7,560 ($21,168) — 48, 115
,, ,, £2,188 ($6,076) — 50
,, ,, £1,276 ($3,573) — 50
,, Hounds, seated. £900 ($2,520) — 58
,, Horse, T'ang. £892 ($2,498) — 116
,, Incense burner. £1,313 ($3,676) — 50
,, Jar. Famille verte. £500 ($1,400) — 39
,, Jar. 14th century. £2,520 ($7,056) — 115
,, Jardinière, celadon. £500 ($1,400) — 38
,, Kuan Yin. £200 ($560) — 40
,, ,, £582 ($1,638) — 50
,, Kylins, turquoise. £984 ($2,755) — 50

Chinese. Lions of Fo. £365 ($1,022) 49
,, ,, £766 ($2,145) 50
,, Parrots. £800 ($2,240) 39
,, Pheasants. £8,800 ($24,640) 24
,, ,, £3,642 ($10,198) 50
,, Plates, Jesuit. £140 ($394) 40
,, Potiches. £457 ($1,224) 50
,, ,, £7,510 ($21,028) 50
,, ,, £5,729 ($16,041) 49
,, ,, £875 ($2,450) 49
,, Pu-tai Ho Shang. £815 ($2,450) 50
,, Dish, Hung Chih. £240 ($672) 39
,, Shrine, celadon. £100 ($280) 38
,, Stem-cup, T'ien Shun. £2,600 ($7,280) 39
,, Toad, turquoise. £1,136 ($3,181) 50
,, Tureen, export. £360 ($1,008) 58
,, Urns, export. £1,856 ($5,200) 28
,, Vase, baluster. £423 ($1,184) 50
,, ,, celadon. £340 ($952) 38
,, ,, ,, £900 ($2,520) 38
,, ,, ,, £400 ($1,120) 38
,, ,, kinuta. £1,750 ($4,816) 58
,, ,, Lung Chü'an. £195 ($546) 38
,, ,, rouleau. £452 ($1,266) 50
,, ,, ,, £750 (2,100) 39
,, Water-pot, celadon. £290 ($812) 38
Ceramics, Japanese. Stag and doe, Arita. £1,155 ($3,234) 48
Ceramics, Persian. Bowl, Rayy. £300 ($840) 21
,, ,, Samarkand. £420 ($1,176) 21
,, Ewer, Rayy. £330 ($924) 21
Ceramics, Turkish. Dishes. £40 ($112) 22
,, ,, £65 ($182) 22
,, Jug. £190 ($532) 22
Enamels, Chinese. Altar set. £1,550 ($4,340) 41
,, Beakers. £210 ($585) 41
,, Bottle. £200 ($560) 41
,, Buffaloes. £1,250 ($3,500) 41
,, Cup and stand. £360 ($1,008) 41
,, Dish. £340 ($952) 41
,, Incense burner. £330 ($924) 116
,, Peach bowl. £700 ($1,960) 41
,, Plate, ruby back. £280 ($784) 115
,, Vases. £550 ($1,540) 41
Furniture, Chinese. Lacquer tables. £360 ($1,008) 21
Ivory, Japanese. Vases, Shibayama. £160 ($448) 40
Jade, Chinese. Boulder. £120 ($336) 24
,, Bowl. £1,600 ($4,430) 42
,, ,, £580 ($1,624) 41
,, Boxes, quail. £160 ($448) 24
,, Brush pot. £2,400 ($6,720) 42
,, ,, £5,000 ($14,000) 42, 139
,, Buffalo. £1,200 ($3,360) 40
,, ,, £6,000 ($16,800) 40
,, Koro. £680 ($1,904) 41
,, Libation cup. £620 ($1,736) 41
,, Lotus. £720 ($2,016) 41
,, Ting. £1,650 ($4,570) 58
,, Vase. £640 ($1,792) 58
,, ,, £90 ($252) 24
Lacquer, Chinese. Panel. £500 ($1,400) 41
,, ,, Screen, Coromandel. £1,784 ($5,000) 44

Lacquer, Chinese Screen, Coromandel. £2,409 ($6,750) 44, 116
Painting, Chinese. Mirror picture. £1,575 ($4,410) 21
,, ,, ,, £1,050 ($2,940) 21, 127
,, Japanese. Kakemono, Hokusai. £280 ($784) 47

Paintings, Drawings, etc.

Amerling, F. von. Caritas. £812 ($2,274) 40
Angelico, Fra. St. Benedict. £9,500 ($26,600) 34
Anghiari Master. Cassone panel. £2,856 ($8,000) 45
Aragonese Master. Altar-piece. £3,570 ($10,000) 45, 75
Bazille, F. Manet dessinant. £1,531 ($4,287) 32
,, Self-portrait. £11,663 ($32,656) 32
Bloemart, Abraham. Tobias and the Angel. £1,155 ($3,234) 22
Boilly, L. L. Mme Chenard. £504 ($1,411) 39
,, Mlle Gerard. £1,995 ($5,586) 39
,, Self-portrait. £1,155 ($3,234) 39
,, Young woman. £1,575 ($4,410) 39
Bonnard, P. Farm at Vernon. £14,175 ($39,690) 29, 82
,, Femme Nue. £18,000 ($50,400) 37, 83
,, Jardin du Peintre. £9,000 ($25,200) 37, 85
,, Jardin publique. £1,531 ($4,287) 35
,, Notes sur l'amour. £6,233 ($17,452) 55
,, Petit route meridionale. £18,958 ($53,082) 35
Bonnington, J. P. Château of the Duchesse de Berri. £6,800 ($19,040) 49
Bosschaert, School of. Flowers. £2,100 ($5,880) 60, 73
Boudin, E. Barques de peche au mouillage. £3282 ($9,190) 35
,, Beach scene. £1,873 ($5,250) 42
,, Beach scene at Berck. £4,200 ($11,760) 29, 86
,, Boats at Dieppe. £4,998 ($14,000) 42
,, Bords de mer. £2,260 ($6,328) 35
,, Plage à Trouville. £9,000 ($25,200) 28
,, Sortie du port de Trouville. £2,260 ($6,328) 35
,, View of Trouville. £5,040 ($14,112) 53
Boucher, F. The Mill. The Trout Stream. £10,500 ($29,400) 36
,, Venus & Cupid. £168 ($470) 40
Braque, G. Barque Pavoisée. £9,500 ($26,600) 37, 82
,, Bords de mer. £4,374 ($11,407) 55
,, Composition: Violin. £51,815 ($145,000) 26
,, Femme au Miroir. £42,000 ($117,600) 41
,, L'oiseau. £2,041 ($5,715) 32
Bronzino, A. Portrait of a Woman. £504 ($1,411) 40
Brouwer, A. Bauern im Wirtshaus. £677 ($1,896) 22
Brueghel, J. Basket of Fruit. £3,000 ($8,400) 53
,, Festival in the Square. £780 ($1,400) 60
,, Flower piece. £15,000 ($42,000) 53
,, Landscape. £1,890 ($5,292) 22
,, St. John the Baptist. £892 ($2,498) 22
Caillebotte. Le tournesols au bord de la rivière. £1,348 ($3,774) 35
Callot, J. Capture of Nancy. £105 ($294) 40
Canaletto. Capriccio. £7,500 ($21,000) 34
,, Grand Canal, Venice. £3,570 ($9,996) 47
,, View of Redentore. £20,000 ($56,000) 23
,, View of S. Giorgio Maggiore. £32,000 ($89,600) 23
Cantarini, S. Flight into Egypt. £682 ($1,910) 39
Cassat, M. Jeune Femme Assise. £5,104 ($14,291) 50
,, Jeune fille au chapeau vert. £7,500 ($21,000) 37

Castan, E.   Kinder im Fruhling.   £338 ($946)   53
Catalan Master.   Lamentation of Christ.   £1,016 ($2,844) 33
Cézanne, P.   La Barque.   £5,766 ($16,145)   32
,,   Les Ivrognes.   £10,000 ($28,000)   37
,,   Les entre des arbres.   £2,843 ($7,960)   32
,,   Mme Cézanne.   £1,100 ($3,080)   37
,,   Maison abandonée au Tholonet.   £38,000
   ($106,400)   47
,,   Le Pêcheur.   £3,353 ($9,388)   32
,,   La Pêcheuse.   £2,552 ($7,146)   32
,,   Les Pommes.   £71,428 ($200,000)   26
,,   Pommes et Bouteilles.   £6,634 ($18,575)   54
,,   Portrait d'homme.   £729 ($2,041)   35
,,   Toits d'une Ferme.   £1,823 $5,104)   54
Chagall, M.   Grand bouquet.   £12,800 ($35,840)   37
,,   Jeunes   filles   avec   fleurs.   £10,573
   ($29,604)   32
,,   Mariés   de   la   Tour   Eiffel.   £5,832
   ($16,330)   55
,,   Portrait de femme.   £1,313 ($3,676)   32
Chirico, G. de.   Les Bestiaires.   £401 ($1,123)   32
,,   Horsemen   on   the   Shore.   £1,260
   ($3,528)   53
Clevely, J.   Launching   a   Man-o'-War.   £1,155
   ($3,234)   39
Constable, J.   Anne Mary Constable.   £5,200 ($14,560)   49
,,   Country road, Dedham.   £2,100 ($5,830)   49
,,   Landscape   with   cloudy   sky.   £2,520
   ($7,056)   46
,,   Landscape   with   shepherd.   £1,575
   ($4,410)   46
,,   Old Barn.   £4,800 ($13,440)   48
,,   Stormy   sky   at   Hampstead.   £2,100
   ($5,830)   46
,,   Suffolk Copse.   £2,100 ($5,830)   46
Corbellini, L.   La Bohemienne.   £357 ($1,000)   42
Corot, J. B. C.   Souvenir d'Italie.   £5,775 ($16,170)   29
Courbet, G.   La Cascade.   £861 ($2,411)   56
Cranach, L.   Adam & Eve.   £6,510 ($18,228)   22
,,   Dr   Johann   Bugenhagen.   £10,000
   ($28,000)   34
Cuyp, A.   Portrait of Boy.   £735 ($2,058)   39
,,   Portrait of Girl.   £1,050 ($2,940)   39
,,   ,,   £609 ($1,705)   23
Dadd, R.   Titania Sleeping.   £290 ($812)   30
Dalby, D.   Huntsmen (pair).   £630 ($1,764)   35
Dauchot, G.   Jockey.   £393 ($1,100)   42
Daumier, H.   Head.   £7,000 ($19,600)   28
,,   Têtes de deux hommes.   £1,520 ($4,256) 37
,,   Wagon   de   troisième   classe.   £2,220
   ($6,216)   28, 82
Defregger, F.   Die Kleinen Sänger.   £434 ($1,215)   53
Degas. E.   Balleteuse.   £1,160 ($3,250)   42
,,   Jeune femme assise avec eventail.   £3,800
   ($10,640)   37
,,   Man on horseback.   £121 ($338)   36
,,   Modiste   garnissant   au   chapeau.   £2,500
   ($7,000)   39
,,   Trois Jockeys.   £23,205 ($65,000)   42, 72
Delacroix, E.   Normandy Horse.   £500 ($1,400)   39
Demorne, J.-L.   L'heureux menage.   £11,663 ($32,656) 51
,,   L'arrivée du Bac.   £2,260 ($6,328)   51
Derain, A.   Barque échouées dans le Pont.   £10,208
   ($28,582)   32
,,   Westminster.   £3,800 ($10,640)   47
Dongen, K. van.   Acrobats.   £2,553 ($7,148)   55
,,   Les Arums.   £5,868 ($16,430)   35
,,   Le Mer.   £5,159 ($14,445)   56

Dossi, Dosso.   Allegorical figures.   £6,071 ($17,000)   78
Dou, Gerard.   Le petit musicien. $984 ($2,755)   31
Drouais, F. H.   Jeune élève.   £2,698 ($7,554)   31
,,   Young girl.   £2,205 ($6,174)   47
,,   (companion picture).   £2,100 ($5,830)   47
Dufy, R.   Deauville.   £1,313 ($3,676)   32
,,   Femme nue assise.   £1,458 ($4,082)   32
,,   Interieur.   £912 ($2,455)   34
,,   Le Pesage.   £1,531 ($4,287)   55
,,   Port de Marseille.   £3,879 ($10,861)   55
,,   Set of 13 water-colours.   £19,000 ($53,200)   47
,,   Vers New York.   £859 ($2,349)   54
Dürer, A.   Maximilien Ier.   £2,260 ($6,328)   31
Dürer (after)   ,,   £607 ($1,700)   45
Dyck, A. van   Earl of Pembroke.   £115 ($322)   39
,,   Jan Malderus.   £2,520 ($7,056)   47
,,   Portrait   of   a   Woman.   £6,300
   ($17,640)   39, 76
Epstein, J.   Child.   £105 ($294)   36
,,   Child with top.   £68 ($190)   36
,,   Hollyhocks.   £210 ($588)   25
,,   Recumbent nude negress.   £58 ($162)   36
,,   Roses.   £290 ($812)   25
Fabriano, G. da.   Madonna and Child.   £945 ($2,646)
   39, 70
,,   Vierge à l'adoration.   £1,830 ($5,124)   55
Fabritius, C.   Rembrandt.   £14,700 ($35,160)   24, 74
Fantin-Latour, H.   Flower   paintings   (pair)   £5,880
   ($16,464)   49
Fedé, G.   Coupe de Fruits.   £875 ($2,450)   55
Flint, Russell.   Julia.   £440 ($1,232)   58
,,   One Summer Day.   £420 ($1,176)   58
,,   Pool of Echoes.   £720 ($2,016)   30
,,   Sands at Bamburgh.   £240 ($672)   58
Fontenoy, B. de.   Flower piece.   £1,600 ($4,430)   46
Fragonard, J.-H.   Le   Baiser   à   la   Fumée.   £1,700
   ($4,760)   23
,,   Bathers.   £4,200 ($11,760)   34
,,   Cache-cache.   £10,934 ($20,615)   31
,,   Le Galant surpris.   £1,750 ($4,900)   31
Friesz, Othon.   Bathers.   £1,470 ($4,116)   53
,,   Les canaux d'Anvers.   £1,823 ($5,104)   55
Gainsborough, T.   Mr   &   Mrs   Robert   Andrews.
   £150,000 ($364,000)   23
,,   Fanny Kemble.   £2,500 ($7,000)   49
,,   Dr Marsh.   £2,400 ($6,720)   49
Gauffier, L.   Duke of Sussex.   £1,150 ($3,220)   46
Gauguin, P.   La Côte Bretonne.   £9,000 ($25,200)   27
,,   Femme assise.   £38,000 ($106,400)   47
,,   La fiancée.   £9,843 ($27,560)   32
,,   Les folie de l'Amour.   £2,200 ($6,160)   37
,,   Tahitienne accroupi.   £3,000 ($8,400)   37
Gelder A. de.   Hermann Boerhave and wife.   £15,000
   ($42,000)   34
Gericault, T.   Le   martyre   de   S.   Pierre.   £1,021
   ($2,858)   55
Gogh, V. van.   Garden at Arles.   £4,000 ($11,200)   37
,,   Paysan travaillant.   £7,292 ($20,418)   56
,,   Roofs at Arles.   £5,000 ($14,000)   37
,,   Viellard   avec   parapluie.   £3,800
   ($16,640)   37
Goya, F.   Old woman.   £1,400 ($3,920)   36
,,   Standing Monk.   £298 ($854)   40
Goyen, J. van.   Bords de Rivière.   £1,750 ($4,900)   31
,,   Château   Loewenstein.   £1,677
   ($4,696)   31
,,   Landscape.   £4,800 ($13,440)   34
,,   ,,   £3,900 ($10,920)   56

Goyen, J. van. Landscape £1,050 ($2,940) 46
,, River Scene. £9,450 ($26,460) 71
,, Valkof Castle, Nijmegen. £4,200 ($11,760) 22
Greco, E. Des letzte Abendmahl. £1,354 ($3,791) 53
Gris, J. Harlequin with a Guitar. £16,000 ($44,300) 47
,, Nature morte. £5,000 ($14,000) 41
,, ,, ,, £2,000 ($5,600) 37
,, Woman with Mandoline. £4,100 ($11,480) 39
Gromaire, M. Nu au fauteuil. £2,844 ($7,963) 55
Guardi, F. Capriccio. £1,470 ($4,116) 40
,, Isola S. Giorgio Maggiore. £3,748 ($10,550) 45, 73
Guillaumin, A. Chemin sous les arbres. £1,094 ($3,063) 55
,, Crozant, le Pont Charraut. £1,202 ($3,366) 35
,, Landschaft in Südfrankreich. £434 ($1,215) 40
,, Potager devant le ferme. £875 ($2,450) 55
,, La Sablière. $839 ($2,349) 55
Guys, C. Amazone et Dandy à Hyde Park. £802 ($2,246) 55
Hals, Frans. Portrait of a Man. £182,000 ($509,600) 53
Hartung, H. Peinture noire et verte. £4,200 ($11,760) 37
Heem, J. D. de. Still Life. £1,000 ($2,800) 46
Herring, Senr J. F. Farm by the Sea. £300 ($840) 30
,, "Flying Dutchman". £1,732 ($4,850) 47
,, "Whisker". £840 ($2,352) 46
Hilaire, J.-B. L'ara. £1,641 ($4,545) 51
Hitler, A. Water-colour. £280 ($784) 28
,, ,, £320 ($896) 28
Hobbema, M. River scene. £14,700 ($35,160) 24, 77
Hoogh, P. de. Kitchen interior. £840 ($2,352) 23
Huysum, J. van. Flower piece. £5,500 ($15,400) 23
Ingres, J. A. D. Nude. £679 ($1,900) 74
Isenbrandt, A. Madonna and Child. £3,500 ($9,800) 34
John, A. Jamaican landscape. £400 ($1,120) 58
,, The Little Kalmuck. £550 ($1,540) 25
,, Sweet Williams. £399 ($1,117) 36
,, Tower and Sky. £294 ($823) 36
Kalf, W. Les Pièces d'Orfèvrerie. £1,495 ($4,186) 55
Kandinsky, W. View of Murnau. £3,800 ($10,640) 39
,, Winter landscape. £5,500 ($15,400) 39
Kauffmann, I. Die neue Zofe. £542 ($1,518) 40
Key, W. Caritas. £338 ($946) 53
Klee, P. Fischzauber. £279 ($784) 92
,, Indischer Blumengarten. £4000 ($11,200) 37
Knight, L. Springtime. £340 ($952) 30
Lacroix, C. F. Italian Coast Scene. £1,260 ($3,528) 39
,, View of Rome. £2,730 ($7,644) 22
Lancret, N. Seated Woman. £550 ($1,540) 23
Laurencin, M. Head of a Woman. £89 ($249) 36
,, Jeune fille aux colombes. £1,276 ($3,573) 56
Lawrence, Sir T. Sarah Siddons. £1,071 ($3,000) 28
Lebourg, A. Les Bords de la Seine. £1,385 ($3,878) 55
,, ,, £1,677 ($4,646) 55
,, ,, £948 ($2,654) 56
,, La Rochelle. £912 ($2,554) 35
,, St Valéry sur Somme. £875 ($11,609) 32
Lepine, S. Bords de Seine. £4,080 ($11,424) 32
,, Le Pont royal. £4,449 ($12,457) 52
Loiseau. Notre Dame de Paris. £729 ($2,041) 35
Lorjon, B. Tournesol séant sur fond verte. £1,495 ($4,186) 56

Luce, M. La Mare. £802 ($2,246) 55
Luini, B. St. Catherine. £1,607 ($4,500) 45
Maillol, A. Female Nude. £58 ($162) 36
Malevich, K. Still life. £1,800 ($5,040) 39
Mallet, J.-B. Le Lecture de la lettre. £1,240 ($3,472) 55
Man, C. de. Der Besuch des Arztes. £609 ($1,705) 22
Manessier, G. Dernier froid. £911 ($2,551) 56
Magnasco, A. Landscape. £10,500 ($29,400) 24, 80
Marcoussis, L. Oslo. £948 ($2,766) 55
Marquet, A. Marché aux Pommes. £4,000 ($11,220) 50
,, Notre-Dame. £5,200 ($14,560) 37
,, Le Pont Neuf. £3,389 ($9,489) 56
,, Port d'Alger. £1,822 ($5,102) 56
Matisse, H. Fille de l'artiste. £3,000 ($8,400) 37
,, Haitian Woman. £803 ($2,250) 42, 89
,, Jeune fille en robe blanche. £7,292 ($20,418) 56
,, La Leçon de Peinture. £21,000 ($58,800) 29, 125
,, Nature Mort. £5,176 ($14,493) 56
,, Paysage de Corse. £4,146 ($11,609) 32
,, Woman with folded arms. £31 ($87) 36
Michelangelo. Panel. £13,000 ($36,400) 53
Michau, T. Von der Schenke. £432 ($1,210) 40
Mignard, P. Mme de Sevigné. £3,791 ($10,619) 51
Miro, J. Composition. £4,376 ($12,253) 32
,, ,, £4,000 ($11,220) 56
,, Woman and Child. £370 ($1,036) 60
Modigliani, A. Beatrice Hasting. £10,000 ($28,000) 37
,, Boy in a green suit. £20,627 ($57,500) 42
,, Boy with red hair. £21,000 ($58,300) 47
,, Caryatide verte. £2,200 ($6,160) 28
,, Leopold Zborowski. £8,500 ($23,800) 28
,, Mme Eyraud-Vaillant. £1,000 ($2,800) 37
,, Mme Lune Czechoswka. £22,000 ($61,600) 41
,, Oscar Mestchianinoff. £38,000 ($106,400) 41
,, Portrait de jeune fille. £24,000 ($67,200) 37, 84
,, Tête de jeune femme. £313 ($876) 34
Monet, C. Femme au bord de la mer. £9,480 ($26,544) 55
,, Grand Canal, Venice. £19,500 ($54,600) 28
,, Le Givre. £8,000 ($22,400) 37
,, Nymphéas. £10,573 ($29,604) 56
,, Rouen. £10,719 ($30,013) 35
,, Water Lilies at Giverny. £18,000 ($50,400) 47
,, Water Garden, Givenchy. £19,950 ($55,860) 29
,, Water Garden, Giverny: Evening. £19,950 ($54,800) 108
Moore, H. Drawing for sculpture. £380 ($1,004) 25
,, ,, £250 ($700) 25
,, Madonna & Child. £900 ($2,520) 58
,, Mother and Child. £320 ($896) 39
,, Standing Nude. £240 ($672) 58
Moreau le Jeune. Fête and Feu d'Artifice. £1,240 ($3,472) 51
Morland, G. Coast scene. £1,800 ($5,040) 23
,, Farmyard scene. £1,300 ($3,640) 23
,, Smugglers. £1,800 ($5,040) 23
,, Stable interior. £500 ($1,400) 23
Mortimer, J. H. Death of Orpheus. £472 ($1,322) 35
Munnings, A. Hop pickers returning. £735 ($2,058) 36
,, Man asleep. £1,050 ($2,940) 36
,, Racing scene. £997 ($2,792) 47
Nain, M. le. The Entombment. £6,090 ($17,052) 39
Nash, P. The Woodshed, Iden. £500 ($1,400) 25

Nattier, J. M. Louis Quinze. £4,223 ($11,824) 55
Neer, van der. Winter landscape. £7,600 ($21,280) 53
Nicholson, B. Heures de Jour. £1,400 ($3,920) 25
,, Playing cards. £1,500 ($4,200) 25
,, Roof tops, St. Ives. £1,700 ($4,760) 37
Ostade, A. van. Der Sautanz. £880 ($2,464) 22
Oudry, J.-B. Gazelle and hounds. £8,800 ($24,640) 23
,, La curée faite. £4,005 ($11,214) 55
Palmer, S. Harvesting scene. £490 ($1,372) 40
,, Weald of Kent. £6,000 ($16,800) 49
Pascin, J. Le Blonde. £1,531 ($4,287) 56
Perronneau, J.-B. Le femme au collier. £2,114 ($5,919) 31
Pettenkofen, A. v. Am Ziehbrunnen. £677 ($1,896) 53
,, Szolnaker Geschirrmarkt. £475 ($1,330) 33
Piazzetta, G. B. Girl. £460. ($1,288) 36
Picasso, P. Coquelicots. £1,166 ($3,265) 55
,, Couple de dos. £12,766 ($35,730) 55
,, Deux Femmes. £11,500 ($32,200) 26
,, Deux femmes marchand. £4,000 ($11,200) 40
,, Faunes et Nymphs. £734 ($2,055) 34
,, Femme accroupie. £48,000 ($134,000) 41, 102
,, Femme assise dans un fauteuil. £5,500 ($15,400) 41
,, Femme se maquillant. £1,677 ($4,646) 56
,, Grand Portrait. £13,250 ($37,016) 26
,, L'homme au gant rouge. £26,000 ($72,800) 41
,, Intérieur Barcelone. £4,229 ($11,841) 32
,, Melon et figures de Barbarie. £3,570 ($9,996) 55
,, Nature morte. £17,000 ($47,600) 41
,, ,, £9,000 ($25,200) 41
,, ,, £20,000 ($56,000) 41
,, Nu endormi. £7,558 ($21,162) 55
,, Nu (La Gommeuse). £30,000 ($84,000) 41
,, La Table. £1,677 ($4,696) 34
,, Trois Baigneuses. £6,000 ($16,800) 37
Pillement, J. Chateau de St Cloud. £2,260 ($6,328) 51
Pissarro, C. Avant Port de Dieppe. £12,495 ($35,000) 42, 88
,, Paysage d'Eragny. £1,100 ($3,080) 37
Pittoni. Adoration. £3,200 ($8,960) 34
Poelenburg, C. von. Moses schlägt Wasser aus dem Felsen. £475 ($1,330) 40
Pol, Ch. van. Fruit et fleurs. £1,080 ($3,024) 55
Pollard, J. North Country Mail. £19,000 ($53,200) 49, 71
Poussin, N. Grateful Father. £1,786 ($5,000) 27
Prud'hon, P. P. Académie de femme debut. £1,312 ($3,674) 51
Realfonso, T. Blumenstück in weiss blauer Fayence-vase. £516 ($1,444) 33
,, Blumenstück mit Grünling. £432 ($1,210) 33
Redon, O. Poissons. £1,700 ($4,700) 37
,, Tête mysterieux. £1,100 ($3,080) 37
Rembrandt. Angel threatening Balaam. £4,800 ($13,440) 23
,, Jésus parmi les docteurs. £1,458 ($4,082) 31
,, Portrait of a woman. £22,000 ($56,560) 23
,, Portrait of a man. £40,000 ($112,000) 23
Renoir, P. A. Baigneuse. £17,503 ($48,008) 32
,, Le Bergere. £10,208 ($28,582) 32
,, Corbeille de Peches. £5,576 ($15,613) 55
,, La Femme au manchon. £4,375 ($12,250) 55

Renoir, P. A. Jeune femme. £3,934 ($11,015) 32
,, Mère et enfant. £38,000 ($106,400) 37
,, Nu debout dans l'eau. £38,000 ($106,400) 47, 90
,, Paysage de Cagnes. £3,200 ($8,960) 37
,, Portrait du peintre H.-L. £2,683 ($7,510) 32
,, Reclining Nude. £16,000 ($44,300) 47
,, Study of Nude. £168 ($470) 36
Reynolds, J. George Hardinge. £1,071 ($3,000) 28
,, Piping Shepherd. £1,365 ($3,822) 46
Robert, H. La Fontaine. £1,458 ($4,082) 31
Robusti, J. See: Tintoretto.
Rodin, A. Nue Allongée. £63 ($176) 36
Romako, A. Hirtenmädchen aus der Campagna. £475 ($1,330) 40
Romney, G. Dorothea, Lady Robinson. £893 ($2,500) 28
,, Sir Edward Every. £2,800 ($7,840) 49
Rouault, G. Nocturne chrétien. £3,499 ($9,797) 5
,, Palais d'Ubu Roi. £14,000 ($39,200) 47
,, Potentate: Pierrot. £12,495 ($35,000) 42, 81
,, Profile de Femme. £9,000 ($25,200) 41
Rousseau, H. Football Players. £37,000 ($103,600) 47
Roux, A. Naval battles (four). £3,642 ($10,198) 55
Rowlandson, T. Port House at Looen. £126 ($353) 39
,, View of Richmond. £504 ($1,411) 39
Ruysdael, J. v. Blick auf Bad Spa. £543 ($1,520) 53
,, An Estuary. £9,450 ($26,460) 47
,, Kühe am Waldweiher. £677 ($1,896) 22
,, Kühe an der Waldfurt. £677 ($1,896) 22
,, Landscape. £8,500 ($23,800) 53
Ruysdael, S. v. Ferry Boat. £15,750 ($44,100) 75
,, Landscape. £7,000 ($19,600) 53
,, Paysage d'Automne. £4,886 ($13,681) 31
,, River Landscape. £3,800 (£10,640) 34
,, River scene. £15,750 ($44,100) 24
Sandby, P. Landscape. £2,100 ($5,830) 47
Sartorius. Hunting scenes (pair). £1,155 ($3,234) 47
Schiele, E. Prison Camp, Mühling. £243 ($680) 53
Schmall, J.-F. Le chat favori. £3,426 ($9,593) 52
Seghers, G. Die Kartenspieler. £338 ($946) 40
Segonzac, D. de. Baie de St Tropez. £1,895 ($5,306) 56
,, En Provence. £3,499 ($9,797) 54
,, Le Guéridon. £2,479 ($6,941) 35
,, Versailles. £437 ($1,224) 32
Seurat, G. Le Phare de Honfleur. £5,000 ($14,000) 37
Shayer, Senr. W. Royal Oak. £651 ($1,823) 35
Sickert, W. Barnet Fair. £840 ($2,352) 29
,, Dieppe. £420 ($1,176) 25
,, ,, £157 ($440) 36
,, La Hollandaise. £105 ($294) 36
,, Marie Bionda. £520 ($1,456) 25
,, Mrs Barrett. £1,500 ($4,200) 58
,, Nude on iron bedstead. £50 ($140) 36
,, Venetian shawl. £100 ($280) 36
Signac, P. Les Andelys. £7,437 ($20,824) 35
,, Fischerbarken bei St. Malo. £516 ($1,444) 33
,, L'Odet à Quimper. £7,655 ($21,434) 35
,, Piazetta, Venice. £786 ($2,200) 86
Sisley, A. Les Lavandières. £11,000 ($30,800) 37
Smith, M. Apples on a wicker chair. £900 ($2,520) 58
,, Landscape. £1,100 ($3,080) 58
,, Portrait of a man. £210 ($588) 36
,, Sleeping model. £750 ($2,100) 58
,, Still life. £550 ($1,540) 58
,, Tiger Lilies. £252 ($706) 36
Snyders, F. Still life. £804 ($2,251) 76

Soulanges, P.   Composition.   £3,000 ($8,400)   37
Soutine, C.   La fille aux canards.   £16,045 ($44,926)   35
,,   L'homme aux rubans.   £14,000 ($39,200)   41
Spencer, S.   The Art Class.   £450 ($1,260)   25
,,   Design Class.   £500 ($1,400)   25
,,   The Garage.   £450 ($1,260)   25
,,   Mary.   £280 ($784)   25
,,   Reclining Nude.   £620 ($1,736)   25
,,   Street in Zermatt.   £1,050 ($2,940)   25
Spinello, P. di.   Vierge de Majesté.   £1,116 ($3,124)   55
Staël, N. de.   Bouteille, poire et cruche.   £9,200
   ($25,760)   37
,,   Nature morte.   £13,000 ($36,400)   47
,,   ,,   £7,558 ($21,162)   55
Steer, W.   Negro Page.   £1,365 ($3,822)   29, 85
Strozzi, B.   Architecture.   £5,000 ($14,000)   68
Stubbs, G.   Baron Roebeck.   £20,000 ($56,000)   23, 53
,,   White Poodle.   £17,000 ($47,600)   23
,,   White Spaniel.   £2,800 ($7,840)   36
,,   Mr & Mrs Wilson.   £4,000 (11,200)   23
Sutherland, G.   Thorn apple flowers.   £400 ($1,120)   58
,,   Vine Pergola.   £460 ($1,288)   25
Teniers, D. (the elder)   L'alchimiste.   £339 ($950)   31
,,   (the younger)   ,,   £2,698
   ($7,554)   31
Thorburn, A.   Black-cock.   £115 ($322)   35
,,   Grouse.   £42 ($118)   35
,,   ,,   £147 ($412)   35
,,   Mallard duck.   £23 ($64)   35
,,   Partridge.   £68 ($190)   35
,,   Robin.   £19 ($53)   35
Tiepolo, G. B.   Feuille d'études.   £510 ($1,428)   51
,,   Virgin and Child.   £620 ($1,736)   36
,,   Vision d'un saint personnage.   £1,750
   ($4,900)   31
Tintoretto.   Portrait of a Prelate.   £5,000 ($14,000)   78
,,   Le Vierge et l'Enfant.   £2,697 ($7,552)   55
Tischbein, J. H. (the elder)
   Le concert dans le parc.   £736 ($2,061)   55
Tissot, J.   Reflections.   £63 ($176)   36
Toulouse-Lautrec, H. de.   Le Coucher.   £25,510
   ($57,428)   55
Troger, P.   Der heilige Karl Borromäus.   £1,624
   ($4,499)   53
Turner, J. W. M.   Aske Hall, Yorkshire.   £3,200
   ($8,960)   49
,,   Lake of Lucerne.   £11,550 ($32,340)   22
,,   Lake of Zug.   £11,025 ($30,870)   22
,,   Llanthony Abbey.   £5,000 ($14,000)
   49, 69
,,   Orford, Suffolk.   £2,730 ($7,644)   35
,,   Port Ruysdael.   £11,068 ($31,000)   80
,,   Vignette.   £300 ($840)   40
,,   ,,   £300 ($840)   40
,,   Windermere.   £2,625 ($7,350)   22
Uccello, P.   Resurrection.   £735 ($2,058)   40
Unattributed.   Arrival and Triumph of a Prince.
   £3,213 ($9,000)   45
Utrillo, M.   Eglise St. Pièrre.   £7,350 ($21,000)   87
,,   Le Lapin Agile.   £5,140 ($14,392)   56
,,   Montmartre.   £2,260 ($6,328)   35
,,   Paris, rue de Clovis.   £3,572 ($10,002)   56
,,   Paysage à le tour.   £3,499 ($9,797)   55
,,   Paysage Parisien.   £1,458 ($4,082)   55
,,   La Rue de la Bonne à Montmartre.
   £2,552 ($7,146)   52
,,   La Tour pointue.   £2,363 ($6,616)   52
,,   Vue de Montmagny.   £1,779 ($4,891)   56

Valadon, S.   Baigneuses.   £300 ($840)   55
,,   Nu debout.   £1,750 ($4,900)   56
Valloton, F.   Nu au miroir.   £452 ($1,266)   52
Valtat, L.   La femme au collier.   £1,313 ($3,676)   35
,,   Portrait de Renoir.   £582 ($1,630)   34
,,   Vase de fleurs.   £1,313 ($3,676)   55
Varley, J.   View of Eton.   £1,850 ($5,180)   50
Victors, J.   Esther, Ahasuerus and Haman.   £630
   ($1,764)   39
Villon, J.   Suzanne Duchamp.   £875 ($2,450)   55
Vinckeboons, D.   Landscapes (pair).   £945 ($2,646)   39
,,   Die spanischen Soldaten.   £402
   ($1,126)   40
Vlaminck, M.   Bords de rivière.   £5,839 ($16,349)   35
,,   Le carrefour.   £4,151 ($11,623)   55
,,   Le champ devant la ferme.   £2,923
   ($8,184)   52
,,   Les femmes.   £3,135 ($8,778)   35
,,   Fleurs dans une vase.   £2,916 ($8,164)   56
,,   Französische   kleinstadt.   £3,385
   ($9,478)   33, 85
,,   Hotel   du   Laboureur.   £7,854
   ($22,000)   42, 88
,,   Marguerites.   £4,299 ($12,037)   52
,,   Paysage.   £3,570 ($10,000)   42, 87
,,   Paysage aux Meules.   £3,317 ($9,716)   56
,,   Le Pont.   £5,322 ($14,902)   50
,,   Rue de village sous la neige.   £3,281
   ($9,187)   55
,,   Vase de fleurs.   £3,135 ($8,778)   52
,,   Le village aux toits rouges.   £1,605
   ($4,444)   55
Vuillard, E.   Femme dans un intérieur.   £1,465
   ($4,102)   55
,,   Intérieur.   £2,326 ($6,513)   56
,,   Interior with family scene.   £4,284
   ($12,000)   42
,,   Jeune fille assise.   £4,400 ($12,320)   37
,,   La Loge.   £11,072 ($31,000)   103
,,   Le malade imaginaire.   £1,250 ($3,500)   42
,,   René Blum.   £4,410 ($12,348)   29
,,   Le sortie des employées.   £2,188
   ($6,126)   35
Ward, J.   Winter landscape.   £4,800 ($13,440)   49
Wet, J. W. de.   Christus.   £537 ($1,588)   78
Wheatley, F.   Conversation piece.   £630 ($1,764)   35
Zoffany, J.   Lavie family.   £7,000 ($19,600)   36

Primitive Art

Benin.   Bronze head.   £262 ($734)   38
,,   Bronze plaque.   £900 ($2,520)   35
,,   Carved tusk.   £950 ($2,660)   35
,,   Ivory figure.   £1,800 ($5,654)   35
,,   ,,   mask   £6,500 ($18,200)   36, 105
French Equatorial Africa.   Wood figure.   £520 ($1,456)   35
Niger Delta.   Wood figure.   £640 ($1,792)   35, 100
Nigeria, S.   ,,   £500 ($1,400)   35

Prints

Bone, M.   Spanish Good Friday, Ronda.   £210 ($583)   57
,,   Rabindranath Tagore.   £26 ($73)   57
Bonnard, P.   Le Bain.   £45 ($126)   57
Braque, G.   Helios II.   £60 ($168)   57
,,   Oiseau sur fond carmin.   £100 ($280)   57, 95
Brockhurst, G.   Adolescence.   £28 ($78)   58
Chagall, M.   Bouquet vert.   £60 ($168)   57
,,   Christ à l'horloge.   £48 ($134)   57
,,   Germain de Prés.   £115 ($322)   57, 94

Gauguin, P. Les Cigale et les Fourmis. £65 ($182) 57
,, Projet d'Assiette. £120 ($336) 57, 95
,, Stephene Mallarmé. £120 ($336) 57, 95
,, Titres du sourire. £45 ($126) 57
Haden, S. Early Riser. £80 ($224) 57
John, A. The Jewess. £14 ($39) 58
,, Serving Maid. £12 ($34) 57
Klee, P. Die Hexe it dem Kamm. £44 ($123) 36
Kokoschka, O. Bildnis. £28 ($78) 57
,, Paul Westheim. £32 ($90) 57
Kollwitz, K. Die Pflüger. £20 ($56) 57
,, Brustbild einer Arbeiterfrau. £28 ($78) 57
McBey, J. Barcarolle. £46 ($129) 58
Marquet, A. Le Port de Boulogne. £168 ($470) 32
Matisse, H. Black Eyes. £95 ($266) 57, 89
,, (after) Les Deux Odalisques. £34 ($95) 57
,, Modèle au fourrure blanc. £122 ($342) 75, 92
,, Nu jambe repliée. £60 ($168) 57
,, Nude with necklace. £65 ($182) 57
,, Odalisque. £110 ($508) 57, 89
,, £68 ($190) 22
Méryon, C. Petit Pont, Paris. £230 ($644) 57
,, Rue des Toiles à Bourges. £60 ($168) 57
Miro, J. Le Jour. £24 ($67) 57
,, Personage. £48 ($134) 57
,, Poster. £38 ($106) 57
Munch, E. Heyerdahl sisters. £85 ($238) 57
,, Portrait of a man. £23 ($64) 36
Picasso, P. Le Chef d'œuvre inconnu. £1,400 ($3,920) 57, 93
,, Crâne sur la table. £108 ($302) 92
,, Nature mort. £70 ($196) 57
,, Le Repas Frugal. £260 ($728) 57, 93
,, Salomé. £160 ($443) 57
,, (after) Les Deux Saltimbanques. £52 ($146) 57
Pissarro, C. Baigneuses luttant. £95 ($266) 57
,, Rue St Lazare, Paris. £50 ($140) 57
Renoir, P. A. Le Chapeau Epinglé. £30 ($84) 57
Rouault, G. Aquatint. £32 ($90) 57
,, Les Clowns. £42 ($118) 57
Toulouse-Lautrec, H. de. Au Hanneton. £270 ($756) 57, 94
,, Femme au Corset. £60 ($168) 57
,, Mlle Marcel Lender. £95 ($266) 57
,, Mlle Pois Vert. £160 ($443) 57
,, Yahne dans sa loge. £96 ($269) 57
Valloton, F. Woodcut. £24 ($67) 57
,, ,, £30 ($84) 57
Valodon, S. Utrillo. £14 ($39) 57
Vlaminck, M. Haystacks. £28 ($78) 57
Vuillard, E. L'atre. £90 ($252) 57
,, Projet de couverture pour une Album d'Estampes. £32 ($90) 57
Whistler, J. McN. Becquet. £23 ($64) 58
,, Black Lion Wharf. £28 ($78) 58
,, Little Dordrecht. £32 ($90) 58
,, Little Nude Model. £34 ($95) 58
,, Rotherhithe. £38 ($106) 58
,, Speke Hall. £52 ($146) 58
Zorn, A. Morna. £36 ($101) 57

Sculpture

Aspetti, T. Peace. £500 ($1,400) 32
Austria. Virgin. £1,489 ($4,169) 53

Bandinelli, B. Cleopatra. £620 ($1,735) 32, 99
Bavaria. St John. £475 ($1,330) 40
,, Saints (pair). £840 ($2,352) 47
Bologna, G. de. Hercules and Anteus. £1,700 ($4,760) 100
Brancusi, C. Two Pigeons. £11,602 ($32,500) 42
Daumier, H. Ratapoil. £1,900 ($5,320) 100
Degas, E. Cheval au galop. £5,100 ($14,280) 37
,, Woman in armchair. £1,680 ($4,654) 101
Eberbach Master. Standing Apostle. £432 ($1,210) 33
,, ,, £203 ($568) 33
Epstein, J. Bernard Shaw. £720 ($2,016) 24
,, Christ (maquette). £800 ($2,240) 24
,, Deirdre. £680 ($1,904) 24
,, Euphemia Lamb. £300 ($840) 58
,, Haile Selassie. £504 ($1,411) 37
,, Head of an infant. £210 ($588) 57
,, Kathleen. £1,250 ($3,500) 42
,, Leda. £550 ($1,540) 58
,, Morna. £800 ($2,240) 24
,, Peggy Jean Asleep. £720 ($2,016) 24
,, Peggy Jean smiling. £400 ($1,120) 24
,, Sholem Asch. £819 ($2,293) 37
,, Somerset Maugham. £500 ($1,400) 24
Flemish. Three Magi. £1,071 ($3,000) 45
,, Woodcarving. 16th century. £330 ($924) 59
Florentine Bellerophon and Pegasus. £250 ($700) 32
French. Bust of Woman. £1,071 ($3,000) 44, 97
German, South. Birth of Christ. £338 ($946) 59
,, Holy Family. £580 ($1,624) 59
,, Mary, Elizabeth, and Zacharias. £402 ($1,126) 97
,, Nymphs (terracotta). £756 ($2,117) 59
,, Putti (torch-holder). £216 ($600) 22, 97
Gothic. Standing Saint. £217 ($608) 33
Holzingen, F. J. St Elizabeth. £217 ($608) 33
,, St Zacharias. £217 ($608) 33
Italian. Jupiter and Apollo. £525 ($1,470) 48
,, Chinoiserie figure. £714 ($1,999) 48
Matisse, H. Deux Negresses. £5,200 ($14,560) 37 *101*
,, Seated Nude. £11,000 ($30,800) 37
Moore, H. Female figure. £5,775 ($16,170) 53
,, Leaf figure. £850 ($2,380) 58
,, Mother and child. £1,500 ($4,200) 58
,, Reclining figure. £1,000 ($2,800) 58
,, Thin reclining figure. £1,200 ($3,360) 58
Picasso, P. Buste d'un Femme. £3,200 ($8,960) 101
Rheims, School of. St Sylvester. £2,052 ($5,750) 44
Riemenschneider, T. Saints. £6,200 ($17,360) 47
Robbia, A. della. Lunette. £4,280 ($40,000) 45, *98*
Rodin, A. Burgher of Calais. £997 ($2,797) 53
,, Eve. £663 ($1,856) 34
,, Romeo et Juliette. £5,500 ($15,400) 37
Sansovino, A. Christ. £250 ($700) 32
Spain. Altar-piece. £5,713 ($16,000) 45, *96*
Tyrol. St Peter. £1,350 ($3,780) 22, *98*
Vischer, P. Neptune. £1,650 ($4,570) 99

Silver, Continental

Bowl & cover. Nürnberg. £819 ($2,296) 121
Brandy bowl. Dutch. £210 ($588) 34
Candlesticks. French. £1,350 ($3,780) 30, *121*
,, ,, £120 ($336) 30
,, ,, £2,916 ($8,164) 52
,, ,, £400 ($1,120) 30
Chalice. Italian. £1,000 ($2,800) 46
Coffee-pot. Norwegian. £700 ($1,960) 20, *117*
,, Swedish. £1,400 ($3,920) 49

Cream-jug. French. £110 ($308) — 40
Cup. Nürnberg. £125 ($406) — 34
Dinner-service. French. £207,000 ($579,600) — 31, *121*
Dishes. ,, £1,456 ($4,077) — 52
Ecuelle. ,, £460 ($1,288) — 59
Ewer. ,, £2,405 ($6,734) — 52
Ewer and stand. ,, £10,573 ($29,604) — 52
Jug & cover. ,, £560 ($1,568) — 30
Salt. ,, £190 ($532) — 30
Salver. Dutch. £220 ($616) — 34
Sconces. Hamburg. £1,071 ($3,000) — 27
Soup-tureen. Austrian. £1,300 ($3,640) — 49
Sucrier. French. £180 ($504) — 30
Tankard. Norway. £1,450 ($4,060) — 49
,, Riga. £108 ($302) — 33
,, Swedish. £800 ($2,240) — 29
,, ,, £440 ($1,232) — 39
,, ,, £1,150 ($3,220) — 34, *112*
Tazza. Augsburg. £380 ($1,064) — 34
Tea-service. ,, £850 ($2,380) — 34
Tobacco box. Dutch. £250 ($700) — 34
Toilet-boxes. ,, £170 ($476) — 30
Vases. Swedish. £480 ($1,344) — 29
Wine-taster. French. £290 ($812) — 30

Silver, United Kingdom
Bowl & dish. £500 ($1,400) — 119
Cake-basket. £510 ($1,428) — 21
,, £3,600 ($10,080) — 39
Candelabra. £420 ($1,176) — 30
,, £1,600 ($4,480) — 26
,, £2,100 ($5,880) — 26
Candlesticks. £5,600 ($15,680) — 46
,, £500 ($1,400) — 34
,, £620 ($1,736) — 26
Casket. £1,500 ($4,200) — 46
,, £8,000 ($22,400) — 120
Casters £820 ($2,296) — 39
Caudle-cup. £2,000 ($5,600) — 22
,, & stand. £678 ($1,900) — 119
Chocolate-pot. £680 ($1,904) — 26
,, £660 ($1,848) — 60
,, £320 ($896) — 26
Coffee-pot. £440 ($1,232) — 20
,, £2,200 ($6,160) — 23
,, £800 ($2,240) — 49
,, £1,300 ($3,640) — 46
,, £1,800 ($5,040) — 46
,, £180 ($504) — 26
,, £500 ($1,400) — 59
Cream-jug. £260 ($728) — 59
Cup. £2,500 ($7,000) — 49
,, £2,700 ($7,560) — 34, 117
,, £6,500 ($18,000) — 23
,, £7,000 ($19,600) — 49, 117
,, £4,800 ($13,440) — 23
,, £520 ($1,456) — 38
,, £680 ($4,704) — 21
,, £1,500 ($4,200) — 38
,, £2,500 ($7,000) — 22
,, £1,550 ($4,340) — 22
Dinner-service. £620 ($1,736) — 59
Dish. £4,100 ($11,480) — 23
,, £250 ($700) — 34
,, £1,750 ($6,160) — 22
Epergne. £420 ($1,176) — 26
Ewer. £4,200 ($11,760) — 46. *119*
,, £1,300 ($3,640) — 46

Flagon. £1,250 ($3,500) — 39
Forks, table. £500 ($1,400) — 20
Fork, 3-pronged. £135 ($378) — 29
Inkstand. £1,800 ($4,940) — 22
,, £3,600 ($10,080) — 23
Jug. £320 ($896) — 34
Monteith. £400 ($1,120) — 26
,, £1,100 ($3,080) — 46
,, £1,050 ($2,940) — 22
,, £964 ($9,700) — 27, *120*
,, £1,050 ($2,940) — 22
Mug. £160 ($448) — 30
Pattern and chalice. £5,000 ($14,000) — 49, *117*
Plates. £550 ($1,540) — 26
Porringer. £300 ($840) — 26
Salt, standing. £3,400 ($9,520) — 46
Salts (set). £200 ($560) — 30
Salvers. £1,250 ($3,500) — 20, *118*
,, £125 ($350) — 26
,, £3,000 ($11,760) — 46
,, £420 ($1,176) — 21
,, £2,200 ($6,160) — 22
,, £480 ($1,344) — 20
Sauceboats. £300 ($840) — 59
Sauce tureen. £780 ($2,184) — 39
Scallop shells. £3,200 ($8,960) — 23
Soup ladle. £250 ($700) — 39
Soup tureen. £3,400 ($9,520) — 46
,, £1,600 ($4,430) — 49
,, £520 ($1,456) — 34
Spice-box. £3,900 ($10,920) — 21
Spoons. c. 1350. £1,450 ($4,060) — 34
,, c. 1514. £1,050 ($2,940) — 20, *117*
,, c. 1575. £340 ($952) — 30
,, c. 1660. £150 ($420) — 30
,, 1699. £500 ($1,400) — 20
,, Apostle. £160 ($448) — 30
,, ,, £210 ($588) — 30
,, Apostle (set). £999 ($2,797) — 30
,, ,, £900 ($2,520) — 59
,, Henry III. £400 ($1,120) — 26
,, ,, £220 ($616) — 30
,, James I. £72 ($202) — 30
Teapot. £2,500 ($7,000) — 46
,, £2,000 ($5,600) — 49, *118*
,, £1,400 ($3,920) — 49, *118*
,, £245 ($686) — 59
,, £500 ($1,400) — 20
Toilet-mirror. £540 ($1,512) — 34
Toilet-set. £2,000 ($5,600) — 46
Tray. £1,606 ($4,500) — 27, *120*
Wine-coolers. £850 ($2,380) — 26
,, £350 ($980) — 26
Wine-cup. £500 ($1,400) — 26

Textiles
Carpets. Agra. £945 ($2,646) — 30
,, Armorial. Louis XVI. £1,250 ($3,500) — 27
,, Aubusson. £520 ($1,456) — 54
,, ,, £620 ($1,736) — 54
,, ,, £1,313 ($3,676) — 31
,, ,, £624 ($1,750) — 141
,, Beauvais. £9,187 ($25,724) — 52
,, Bokhara. £220 ($616) — 54
,, Chinese. £260 ($756) — 54
,, ,, £500 ($1,400) — 59
,, Goa. £2,995 ($8,386) — 36
,, Heraz. £540 ($1,512) — 54

Carpets. Hispano-Arab. £1,606 ($4,500)   45
    ,,   Ispahan. £504 ($734)   53
    ,,   Kashan. £262 ($734)   53
    ,,   ,,   £540 ($1,512)   49
    ,,   Kirman. £273 ($764)   53
    ,,   ,,   £340 ($952)   54
    ,,   Persia. £3,213 ($9,000)   45
    ,,   ,,   £2,856 ($8,000)   45
    ,,   Spanish. £3,045 ($8,526)   141
    ,,   Tabriz. £546 ($1,529)   53
    ,,   Savonnerie. £1,100 ($3,080)   60
Rugs. Azerbaijan. £800 ($2,240)   21, 144
    ,,   Indo-Persian. £360 ($1,008)   21
    ,,   Kashan. £700 ($1,960)   32. 144
    ,,   Nahim. £270 ($756)   54
    ,,   Samarkand. £350 ($980)   60
Tapestries. Armorial 16th century. £11,603 ($32,500)   143
    ,,   Aubusson 18th century.   £846 ($2,369)   31

Tapestries. Aubusson Louis XI. £360 ($1,008)   54
    ,,   ,,   ,, XVI. £1,000 ($2,800)   32, 142
    ,,   Beauvais (Behagle). £1,522 ($4,262)   59
    ,,   Brussels. £540 ($1,512)   49
    ,,   Brussels c. 1500. £3,213 ($9,000)   45
    ,,   ,, 16th century. £4,463 ($12,500)   45
    ,,   Flemish. £405 ($1,134)   53
    ,,   Louis Seize. £750 ($2,100)   54
    ,,   millefleurs c. 1510 £6,248 ($17,500)   45
    ,,   Mortlake. £530 ($1,484)   21
    ,,   ,,   £2,940 ($8,232)   21, 142
    ,,   Sheldon Map. £4,200 ($11,760)   141
    ,,   Soho. £900 ($2,520)   21, 143
    ,,   Touraine. c. 1505. £2,500 ($7,000)   45
    ,,   ,,   ,, £5,712 ($16,000) 45, 141
    ,,   ,,   ,, £1,748 ($5,000)   45
    ,,   Tournai. £670 ($1,876)   21